Christmas 1954.

Mary Scott.

Joypahar,
Chittagong.
E. Pakistan

from
Gladys Cann.

Christmas
Lasts
For Ever

Set and printed in Great Britain by
Tonbridge Printers Ltd., Peach Hall Works,
Tonbridge, Kent,
and Published by
Blandford Press Ltd., 16 West Central St.,
London, W.C.1

CHRISTMAS LASTS FOR EVER

Compiled by
HANNEN FOSS

London
BLANDFORD PRESS

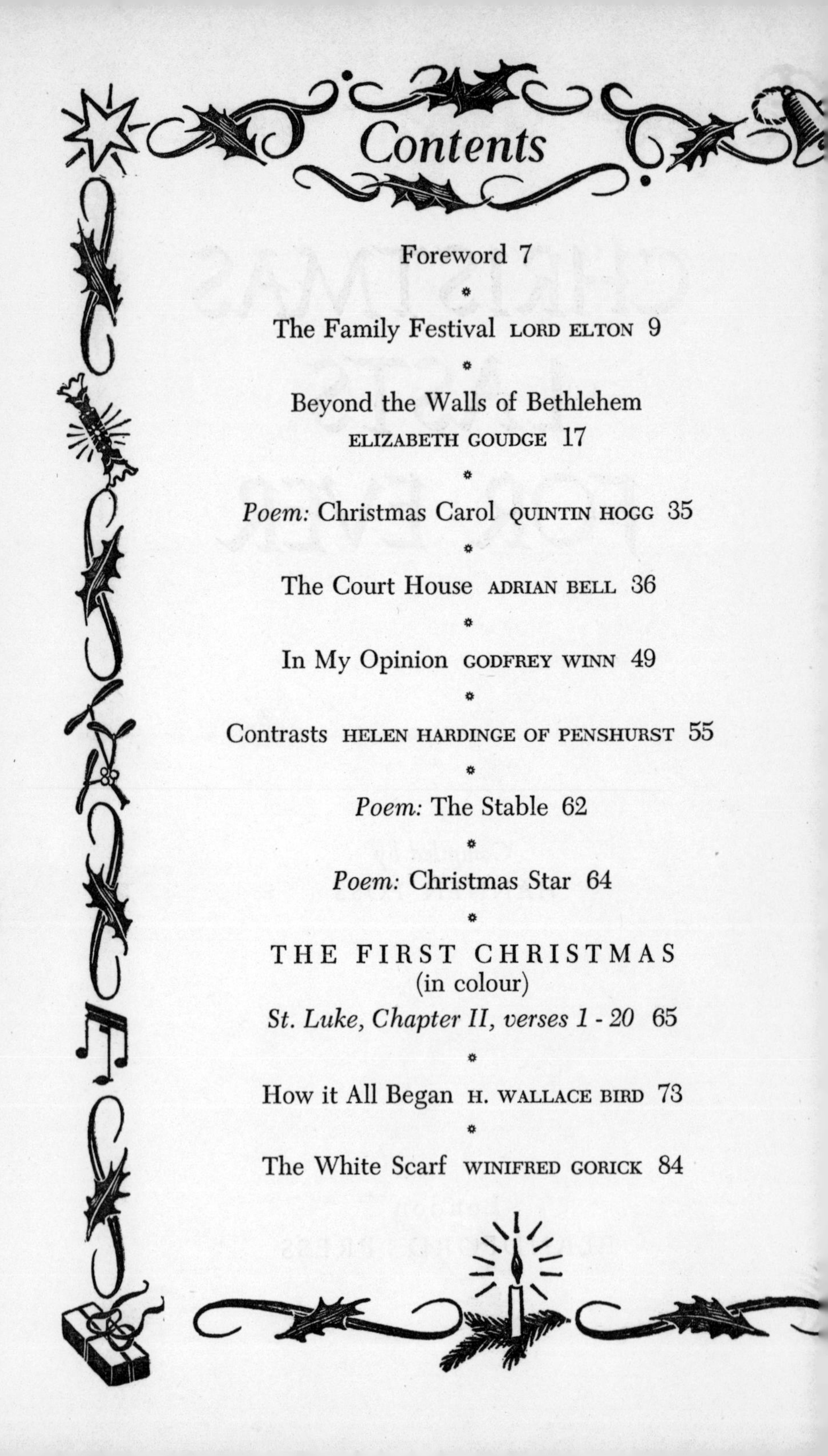

Contents

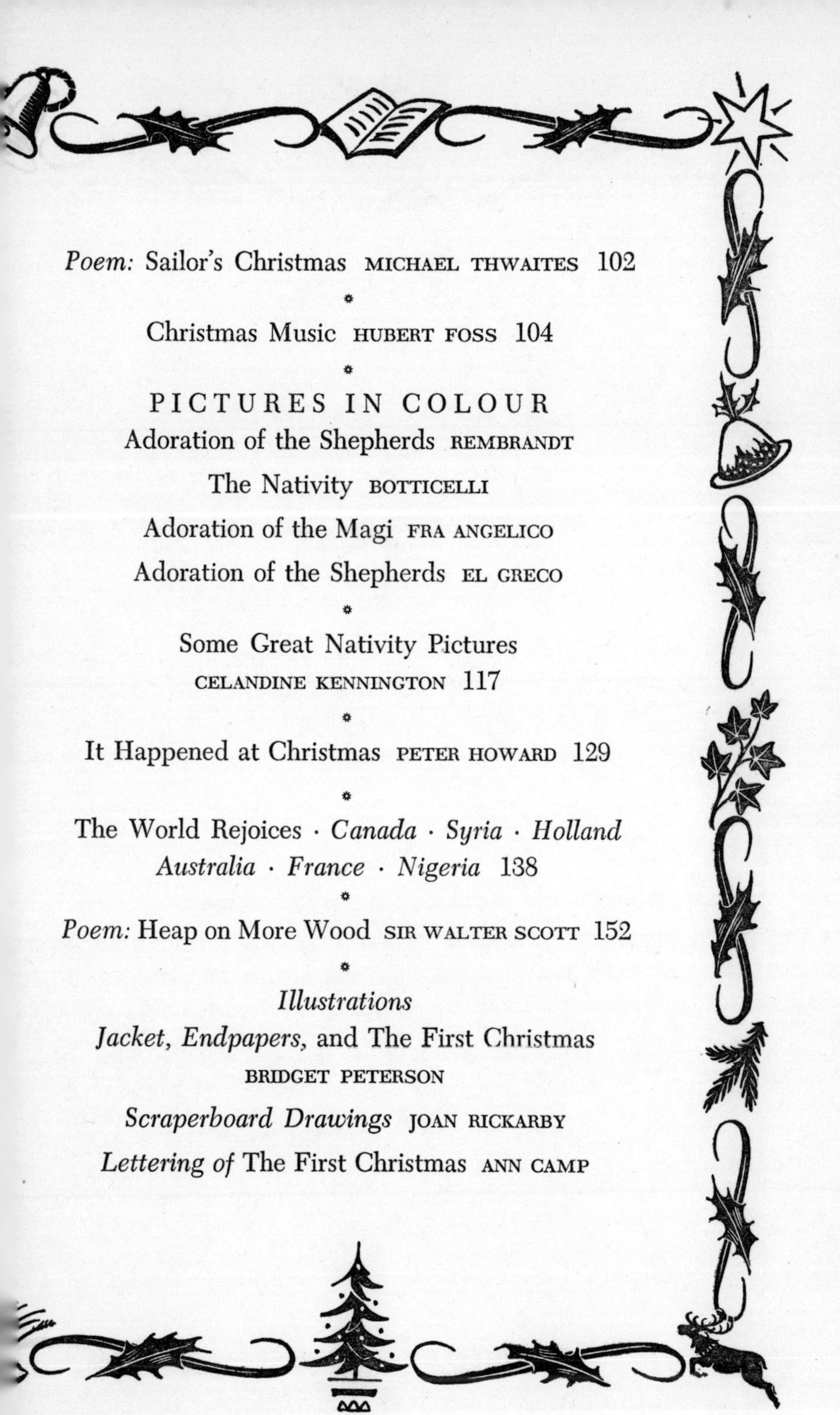

Foreword

IS Christmas more than Christmas pudding?

I remember once shortly before my last Christmas in the Army we were sitting round the table in the mess, having finished lunch. The adjutant, a somewhat harassed man, exclaimed, "I don't know why everyone is trying to get leave for Christmas. They won't get half so much to eat at home as they will here."

That made me think. Is Christmas just a time of feasting and drinking and conviviality, which you can do as well, or better, in the Army as at home? Or is it enormously more?

And I realised that while the very best of material things are liberally poured out at Christmas time, the most precious things of Christmas are not material ones at all.

Christmas is the richest event in the year's calendar. Each age has added to it, till for every one of us Christmas is a warm, cheerful, inspiriting festival, strengthening us on our way into the new year. At the heart of winter, it glows with firelight, candlelight and starlight.

It is primarily a family festival. Everywhere families meet and relations call round to see one another. That has been so ever since the strange, heart-stirring drama of the first Christmas when, under a harsh dictatorship, a lonely man and his wife due to give birth to her first child, struggled eighty miles through the winter's cold to their home town, there to find no welcome, no heart warm enough to offer a fit place for the baby to be born. But to the place where that child was born, came people from far and near and a family and love grew in that stable.

Christmas is a rich human experience when our generosity gets some exercise, jollity invades every place and everyone, even the frostiest puts on the spirit of goodwill. The birth of Christianity is celebrated with the best of everything—best food, best drink, best fun, best presents, best behaviour, best nature. How right that is. Christianity is essentially everything at its very best.

And, willy-nilly, however hardened or disbelieving we may be, for all of us it is a time of spiritual experience. We all come closer to appreciating the love of God. A love for one another stirs more powerfully than at any other time. The music of Christmas, the families united with a glow of goodwill, the good things of every sort surrounding us bring into being a Spirit—the Spirit of our best selves, the people we might have been yet somehow never quite have been. The magic of the first Christmas still invades us, when a Babe was born Who loved all mankind—and we love Him, for who can help loving a small baby?

Somehow at Christmas we feel anything is possible and a Spirit fills our hearts which defies the materialism that threatens to engulf us all. Today isms and philosophies claim men's minds. Yet the simple Spirit of Christmas has a message for the world —a world philosophy, one that claims the heart. Perhaps the answer to the international conferences that bring no cure might be to stage one at Christmas. Even the most hostile statesmen might melt in its atmosphere.

Christmas is meant not only to enrich us as individuals and families but to knit the world together. Men take new heart then—nations can too. What a new factor for statesmen, when, from the richness and fulness of Christmas, nations go into the New Year with new hearts, new faith and new generosity.

H. F.

The Family Festival

by LORD ELTON

EXAMINE the Christmas card of today and you will find it is a most significant production. Turn over an average trayful in an average shop and you will observe that scarcely any of them bear the least relation to Christmas. True, if you look closely you will find a version of the familiar legend, "a Merry Christmas and a Happy New Year," but as far as the picture is concerned—and after all the essence of a Christmas card is the picture—the trayful, you will be forced to conclude, might have been designed to celebrate almost anything but Christmas. There will be bouquets of flowers, summer landscapes, old views of London or Brighton, renderings, faithful or impressionistic, of cats and dogs, deer or even giraffes, and reproductions of a still-life or an Interior by some Dutch Old Master, or of an eighteenth-century French *fête champêtre* by Watteau or Fragonard. But in all this you will observe, there is no Christmas. It would seem indeed that these expensive pieces of pasteboard might just as well have been designed to celebrate a flower show, an Oddfellows' outing, or an August Bank Holiday. And if here and there you chance to come across some apologetic suggestion of Christmas, it will be of the season, not the festival; a coaching-scene in a snowstorm perhaps, or a carouse of rubicund hunting men, not the wise men and the star, or the manger at Bethlehem. Only in exceptional and specialized shops can you rely nowadays on coming upon a Christmas card apparently designed for a Christian festival.

Now the change which has come over the character of

Christmas cards during the last fifty years, though of trifling importance in itself, is a symptom of great social significance. For some while Christmas has been becoming steadily more pagan. In a sense, we may say, it has been reverting to type. For the Christian festival is of course superimposed upon a much older pagan rite. The date of the Birth of the Babe is also the date of the rebirth of the year, the turning-point at which the days begin to lengthen, and life begins to stir again within the earth. There is nothing essentially Christian about the feasting and carnival of Christmas. The mid-winter carouse is a universal pagan tradition, descending from the remotest past. We should have known the false nose, the paper hat and the post-prandial sense of repletion, even if there had never been a Christmas. Christians took over the immemorial tradition of mid-winter merrymaking, and consecrated it. It was right that Christians should make merry, but it was right also that they should remember that they were commemorating a Birth. And for centuries Christians made merry and remembered. Today we still make merry, but as a nation we do not, to the extent or in the same way, remember.

This change in our habits involves an immense loss in itself, a debasement and diminution of the whole festival, which we can ill afford. But it represents also a much greater loss at a much profounder level. As to the injury to Christmas, to the day itself, this is only too evident.

Christmas is the feast of the Child, and therefore of children. Children are not treated with special generosity and consideration on Christmas Day merely because it is agreeable to give them presents, or because it is the prerogative of children to enjoy themselves. They are the centre of the occasion primarily because the whole story of Christmas is a reminder of the special sanctity of childhood. Moreover from the days of Christ, who held up childhood as a model for His disciples—*except ye be converted and become as little children ye shall in no wise enter the Kingdom of Heaven*—to those of Wordsworth and the

Ode on Intimations of Immortality, who believed that *trailing clouds of glory do we come,* and hailed a young child as "Seer blest," not only a special sanctity but a special power of vision has been attributed to childhood. And there can be no doubt that in some ways and at some times children do see more clearly, and see further, than their elders. There are indeed theophanies which are accorded only to children—and to saints. Perhaps it is partly this mysterious insight which accounts for the child's devotion to the story of the first Christmas. And certainly memory suggests that there was a profound if subtle difference between the Christmas of childhood and those of later life. I recall the stocking and the tree vividly enough in all conscience, the church bells almost as clearly, the feasting, curiously enough, scarcely at all. But what lives on in memory as the very essence of the day is none of these. There always came a moment, as I made my expectant way by candlelight from my bedroom to my parents' for the early-morning ritual of the examination of the stocking, when I would catch a glimpse of the still darkling sky, and a star or two above the fir trees. And always there would be borne in on me a sudden profound sense of mystery, as if this day had for once partly lifted the veil between our world and an immense and watchful Presence. The sudden moment of vision did not return as the familiar ritual of the day was re-enacted, yet it remained the mysterious background of all else, and even while the candles blazed on the tree I was conscious of the dark firs without, and of the stars, and the Presence inter-penetrating all.

But even without the piercing candour of the child's vision, which may enable it to see further than its elders into the story of Bethlehem, it must instinctively feel at home with the manger and the animals, the shepherds and the angels, the wise men and the moving star. And for the child brought up upon the gospel story the dear and familiar ritual of Christmas stocking and Christmas tree glows with an added magic because enacted against the background of Bethlehem.

What would Christmas be without its carols, and what are Christmas carols if they cease to be a profession of faith? How great a deprivation when Christmas is cut off from its roots, and shrinks into a mere pretext for jollification and vague benevolence! And not for children only. An occasion which means no more than overspending and overeating, the gross twentieth-century equivalent of the immemorial pagan feast of the reborn year, reduces the adult Christmas also to mere self-indulgence.

It has been wisely said that the moral code of western civilization is still founded upon Christmas ethics, even where the Christian faith has been long abandoned—the toughest young bruiser unthinkingly accepts the convention that a man should not be hit when he is down, or the slogan "Women and children first," though he may know nothing of the Christian teaching out of which they originally grew—but that, though we can no doubt live for a while upon our capital, the moral code is not likely to survive for many generations the faith from which it once sprang. And it is the same surely with Christmas. Sever the tradition from its Christian roots, and the gentler and less earthy elements in it are not likely to survive for long.

There are thus three possible levels at which Christmas can be celebrated. There is the Christian Christmas proper, which is rejoicing founded upon an act of worship and thanksgiving. There is what we may call the semi-Christian Christmas, a survival from the age of faith, which still cherishes those more civilized aspects of the Christmas tradition which are in fact the fruit of its Christian origin, still observing at least a great day of childhood and the home. And there is the purely pagan Christmas, which we can see being celebrated on any twenty-fifth of December by parties of half-intoxicated adults in hotels.

There is surely a special tragedy just now in any decay of the festival of the home. For the home, which has always been the centre of Christian civilization, was the first and most tragic casualty of the late war. Conscription and evacuation dealt the first deadly blows, and what the war undermined, the drab, ambiguous years of peace have so far done singularly little to restore. Increasingly the State intrudes to replace the parent. The statistics of divorce mount steadily, and every divorce means not only the end of a home, but possibly children adrift from their moorings and all the less likely therefore to become in due course successful homemakers themselves. Moreover, the home and the family, which in the nineteenth century suffered from the callousness of the then fashionable individualism, are threatened today by the callousness of a collectivism apparently set on regimenting youth and obliterating the responsibilities of parents. At such a time there is a special need that the festival of the family and the home should revive, and an obvious danger that it may decline.

And there are other senses in which Christmas stands for traditions which, to our loss, have gone out of fashion. For it is the season of the small and the intimate, and ours is the age of the vast, the public and the impersonal. Christmas means the fireside instead of the factory, the lighted tree in place of the cinema, and the laughter of the family instead of the roar of the stadium. And is not that intimacy—Dickens thought of it as cosiness—very near to the heart of its secret? More and more, outside the home, men and women tend to become mere planners' fodder, the bloodless collective material of graphs and statistics—just one more member of the Big Union, another nameless representative of such and such an income group to be canvassed by Investigators of Public Opinion; a combination of numerals and letters on an identity card. The individual is disappearing. Our very language bears witness to the change. Are not officials beginning to speak of bad citizens as unsocial elements, promising soldiers as potential officer material, and men and women who work in factories as industrial personnel?

Contrast one of Dickens' novels with its crowded gallery of eccentrics, each so completely and so unmistakably an individual, with the dreary modern masterpiece whose hero is not a man but a movement, a class, or an institution. Or compare a thatched cottage set in its own flowery patch with a modernistic barrack of workmen's flats opening on to the roaring streets. You will find all these contrasts embodied in the gulf between Thomas Hardy's village choir singing carols under the stars before the lonely farmhouse and the loudspeaker in a cocktail-bar, bellowing the latest distorted jazz to ten million invisible listeners.

The current which bears us towards the vast and mechanical, and away from the human and intimate, has been flowing for a great while now. Ever since the industrial revolution it has been assumed that economic activities are the chief end of human life, and it is only natural that the machine should have come to overshadow, or rather to replace, the man. Indeed all the fashionable philosophies tend to see men as machines. The nineteenth-century agnostic Radical believed that man would be perfectly virtuous and happy if only he were free to live according to his instincts. The twentieth-century agnostic Socialist believes that man will be perfectly virtuous and happy if only the correct environment is planned for him from above. For both, man is a machine, either actuated mechanically by his instincts or responding mechanically to his environment. But the nineteenth-century agnostic forgot that man is a fallen creature, and that free play for his instincts usually means free play for pride, greed and lust. And the twentieth-century agnostic forgets that since man possesses a soul he is visited by impulses from beyond the visible world; and that there can be devils in parsonages and saints in slums.

Paradoxically enough the habit of measuring always by the standards of the machine and the products of the machine spread rapidly during the war in which, as the climax of two centuries of growing materialism, western civilization blew itself to pieces. By now when they said "a higher standard of living" they meant not, as might have been supposed, better morals, but larger incomes. And by that "better Britain," which was so recklessly promised as a direct consequence of the most destructive war in history, they meant not, as the words suggest, a more virtuous Britain but a more comfortable one. If we could accustom ourselves to seeing through the material trappings of Christmas to its spiritual core, we should have taken a considerable step towards solving the world's material problems. Partly of course because the core of Christmas is the core of Christianity, and anyone who has had the experience of living in contact with that rare exception, a wholeheared and practising Christian, will remember the irresistible impression one receives from such persons, of wisdom, goodness and power. Indeed if ever even fifty-one per cent of our population should be genuinely Christian our problems will mostly have solved themselves.

But there is another reason why a people which rediscovered the real Christmas would also not only enjoy Christmas itself as never before but be well on the way towards setting its material house in order. For history abundantly confirms that supreme warning of the New Testament to statesmen—*seek ye first the Kingdom of God and all these things shall be added unto you.* It has indeed been the men who fixed their eyes on another world who have been responsible for the most solid benefits of this world. The great builders of the middle ages, Cromwell and the Puritans, Wilberforce and the Evangelicals who abolished slavery, Wesley and his friends, the source to which so many nineteenth-century reform movements can be traced—these were all men who were primarily concerned with life hereafter, yet they are also the men who most lastingly improved life here. It would seem that because they fixed their eyes on heaven, "all these things" were in fact "added unto them."

And by way of contrast, during the last century and a half men have fixed their eyes more unwaveringly than ever before on earth, ever more confident that they are the captains of their own destiny, capable of building the New Jerusalem of material prosperity here and now. And the result is the world we see around us, an unprecedented aggregate of suffering and insecurity. Fix your eyes on earth, it would seem, and even that you will lose; fix your eyes on heaven, and you will gain earth into the bargain.

And it is the same with the microcosm of Christmas. Treat it as a mere opportunity for jollification, and it will not be long before jollification begins to pall. Treat it primarily as a festival of the spirit, and it will become a festival indeed. And if we could learn to perceive the spiritual truths of Christmas we should at least be a stage nearer to perceiving the spiritual truths of the universe. Christmas indeed might become a school of wisdom in which we should begin to learn to turn away from that ferocious concentration upon earth, which, as it now begins to appear, has lost us not only heaven but earth as well. And indeed if we ever see that spiritual revival, in which, as many believe, lies our chief hope, one of its earliest manifestations might well be a widespread return to the Christian Christmas. For the Christian Christmas was universally popular for many centuries, and still partly survives, so that the current of reviving spiritual life might well flow first into this channel. And certainly there could be no more appropriate medicine for our most deadly spiritual diseases; for the virtue which we most conspicuously lack is humility, and after that we stand most in need of other-worldliness, or the sense of eternity. And the story of Bethlehem is conspicuously a sermon on both these themes. Perhaps if we could catch a prophetic glimpse of the Christmas cards of 1970, we should find that once again they bore some relation to Christmas.

Beyond the Walls of Bethlehem

by ELIZABETH GOUDGE

I

THE Egyptian slave Iras was a strange girl, and already, though she was only fifteen years old and had been an exile from her native country for a bare three years, she bore the marks of the exile in body, mind and spirit. Secretive was her spirit, folded in upon her memories like the petals of a closed flower about its heart; her mind bitter with frustrated longing, her small brown body thin and worn with her grieving.

Her memories never faded, for they were kept fresh by her dreams. When she slept she saw again the old grey town where she had been born, hollowed out of a rocky hill in the desert, with the cool palm trees, the orange groves and the clover fields spread about it, watered by the wells that made this oasis an earthly paradise in the surrounding plain. And she heard the songs that were sung there at evening and felt her mother's arms about her, and watched through the orange blossom that grew in pots in the high window of her home for the return of her father's caravan, winding towards her over the golden sand. . . . But when by day she remembered that caravan she wept, for it would never turn homeward again. Her father had been killed in this country of her slavery, and she, travelling with him, had been there when he died.

It had been a day of sunshine pouring from a burning sky

when she and her father had set out from their home for the land of the Hebrews. She had sat proudly before her father on his trotting camel, and about them had ridden an armed guard with swords and daggers, for the pack camels had been laden with goodly merchandise, spices, fringed girdles, rich silk embroideries, and necklaces of flower-tinted, round glass beads. Many of these lovely things had been fashioned by Iras's mother, and Iras herself had cunningly threaded some of the beads. She had loved threading them, and had begged her father to take her with him one day when he rode to the land of the Hebrews to sell them to the wives of the Roman conquerors who lived there in the new white villas, among the ancient olive groves of that turbulent little land.... It would be madness to take the child, Iras's mother had said, the journey was much too dangerous.... But Iras had begged so hard that her father had yielded and she had gone.

It had been a wonderful journey across the desert; wonderful sun-drenched days swinging along between the burning blue and the burning gold; wonderful nights when her father first checked their course by the stars and then lay down to sleep beneath them, she lying beside him, his cloak flung over them both, his hand within reach of her groping fingers if she should feel afraid in the dark. But she had never felt afraid. His very presence had seemed a surety against all disaster. He and she had laughed together at her mother's fears when the journey was safely over and they were trotting along the fine new Roman road within an hour's journey of their first halting-place, the Hebrew town of Bethlehem.

And it had been just at this moment, when they had felt so safe, that disaster had come upon them. Her father's camel had fallen lame. He was a valuable beast and her father would not press him. The caravan, that had been swinging along at so brisk a pace, had been halted to a slow walk.

"It will be dark before we reach Bethlehem," had said one of her father's servants warningly.

"No matter," had laughed her father. "We are on the high road and the summer stars are bright."

But lest Iras should feel fear he had put an arm about her and sung one of the songs of their country very softly to her alone, the song that the Pharaoh Aknaton had written in praise of the God Who is One. Yet Iras had felt unaccountably afraid as the veils of the twilight dropped about them and a cold little wind blew down from the bare high hills. When they had reached a grove of olive trees that arched over the road, and darkness fell, her fear had deepened to something like panic. . . . But her father had continued to sing, and his singing was the last clear memory she had of him.

The robbers had swept down upon them with the suddenness of some violent storm. At one moment there had been no sound except the clop-clop of the camels' feet on the road, the sighing of the wind in the olive trees and her father's singing, and the next moment the air had been filled with shouts and curses, the screaming of the camels and the thud of blows. A wild form had leaped at her father, a knife gleaming in his hand, and she had been flung off the plunging camel into a bank of flowers growing beside the road. She had lain there, stunned and terrified, and it had seemed that for hours the fight had raged about her, until at last there had been silence again and she had heard the wind sighing in the trees.

And then a hand had fallen upon her shoulder, shaking her, and she had sat up among the flowers, one arm raised to shield her face from blows. In the gleam of torchlight a man had been bending over, a man with a dark keen face who wore shining armour over a scarlet tunic, a scarlet cloak flung over one shoulder and a helmet on his head. The light had gleamed upon the armour of other men, dressed like himself but less richly, and upon what had looked like bundles of torn rags flung untidily upon the road. But these last she had not seen very clearly because the man who had shaken her had moved quickly to stand between her and them. She had lowered the arm she had raised to protect herself, for though she had not been able to understand a word of what he said she had recognized the kindness in his eyes.

II

And so it was that Iras came to be a slave to Claudia, the wife of the Centurian Lucius, whose fine white Roman villa had been built among the olive groves beyond the walls of Bethlehem. He and his men had been too late to save the lives of the merchants, but they had saved Iras. She was not very grateful. Even when she had come to understand the languages of this country, both the Roman tongue and the Hebrew tongue, and had become accustomed to the life of a slave in the beautiful villa, she was still not grateful. She was an exile. The only song of the Hebrew country that she would consent to sing to her mistress was the one that began, "By the waters of Babylon we sat down and wept when we remembered thee, O Sion." For the rest she sang the songs of her own country: the song of the ripe wheat rippling in the wind in the valley of the Nile in Egypt, the song of the water lilies that grew in the great pools about the palace of Pharaoh, and the song her father had been singing when he died. Claudia liked Iras to sing to her, for she had a sweet little voice like the chirrup of a bird. In her careless way Claudia was fond of the child. She always took her with her when she was carried in her litter to Bethlehem, to amuse herself by buying flowers and fruit and vegetables at the booths that edged the narrow paved streets of the little city. . . . It was during one of these expeditions that Iras found the baby, and the whole of her life was changed.

It was a bright clear day in late winter, with spring not far behind, when Claudia in her litter, with an armed guard and a few favourite slaves about her, went down through the olive trees and along the road to Bethlehem.

From a distance, built on its little hill among slender cypress trees, Bethlehem looked a city of another world, enchanted and unearthly; but when you got there, and passed under the dark gateway in the city wall, it was a crowded, smelly, noisy little place with people jostling each other up and down the narrow streets where the latticed wooden windows, built out from the old stone walls of the houses, nearly met overhead, while down below the bright wares were set out before the dark recesses of the shops. But Iras loved it. One eastern hill town is much like another, a natural outgrowing from the rocks and caves that were there already as a shelter for the foxes and the conies. Bethlehem was not so different from the hill town of Iras's birth. When she was there she felt almost as near home as she felt in her dreams.

On this particular day Claudia was full of vigour, and settled down to an enjoyable bout of bargaining with a very old woman who was selling some attractive little cakes, set out upon green leaves spread on a little carpet of scarlet and blue, at the entrance to a cave that was also a small shop.

"You made them, old dame?" asked Claudia, tasting one. She spoke with some astonishment, for the cakes were delicious and daintily displayed, while the shop behind them was a very poor little shop, and the old woman lame and feeble.

"Great lady, my lodger made them," said the old dame, with a gesture of her head towards the flight of rough stone steps that led up to a little house built over the cave. "She has lodged with me since the time of the taxing. It's a hard thing, great lady, that poor people should be forced to travel so far to be taxed. All the way from Nazareth did Mary and her husband come, and she, poor soul, with her hour near at hand. Her babe was born in the inn stable, there being no room in the inn. Poor shift she had, till her man found her this lodging here with me. I say, great lady, it is a hard thing that poor people should be made to travel so far——"

"That will do," interrupted Claudia, sharply. As the wife of a Roman centurion she could not stand here listening to criticism of the government, however well-founded, and the old dame was of the garrulous sort who might go on for hours.

"Run up the steps, Iras," she said, "and find this Mary, and ask her if she can make me a batch of these cakes once a week."

And Iras ran up the steps, and knocked at the door at the top, and lifted the latch and went in.

III

The small arched stone room was full of the sunshine that streamed through the open lattice window. It was neat and clean, with the floor well scrubbed and the rugs that were used as beds at night neatly rolled in one corner. By the window sat Mary, stitching at a little garment, and in a cradle beside her lay her baby, playing with his toes. He was the happiest, most perfect baby Iras had ever seen, and with a cry of delight she knelt beside the cradle and held out a finger to him. He clutched it strongly and purposefully, as a small baby will, and laughed at her. His pretty young mother laughed too, and threaded a piece of scarlet thread into her needle. She did not seem at all surprised to see Iras; evidently she was quite accustomed to having complete strangers coming in at all hours to admire her baby; but she looked at her with quick motherly compassion, and her glance was as embracing as the grip of the baby's tiny hand on Iras's finger. Suddenly Iras felt that she belonged with these two, that where they were was where she wanted to be. For three years she had been an exile, but now, though her body was still in an alien land, her soul had come home.

She forgot all about Claudia's cakes, and almost before she had realized it she had told Mary about her distant home, and Mary had told her about hers, and they were friends. And then she sat in a patch of sunshine on the floor, the baby in her arms, and she felt warm and comforted through and through, body and mind and soul.

But all too soon another of the slaves came clattering up the steps, and banged at the door, and called to Iras that the lady Claudia had gone home, and was very angry that Iras had been so long, and she was to order the cakes quickly and follow her mistress. And Iras jumped up, fear in her eyes, for the slaves were sometimes beaten when they displeased Claudia, and did as she was bidden, and went away.

IV

But she came again. She came once a week to fetch the little cakes that Mary made for Claudia, and though she dared not stay too long with Mary and her baby those days became the days when she really lived. The time between was just a sort of waking dream that linked the great days as the thread of a jewelled necklace links the jewels together.

Upon one of these dream days she sat at evening with Claudia in her warm, luxurious, scented room and sang to her as she lay on the lovely silk cushions of her divan. It was peaceful and still, with twilight gathering outside and the flame of Claudia's little lamp burning like a flower in its silver dish, and Iras sang the Pharaoh Aknaton's song in praise of the One God, and while she sang she thought of the baby and wondered if he was asleep now, and if Joseph had finished his day's carpentering and was sitting with Mary beside the latticed window, watching the last of the sunset before they unrolled their mats and lay down to rest. And Claudia thought of Rome, the lovely city of her birth that she had left for love of her husband, and wept a few homesick tears into her cushions. But she was not really unhappy, and neither was Iras. The twilight was soft and beautiful and the flame of the little lamp burned like a flower.

Into this moment of peace, this women's hour, there came suddenly trampling the Centurion Lucius, loud-voiced, angry, the mud caked upon his boots and the reek of the stables clinging to his cloak. He flung his sword into one corner of the room, his helmet into the other, and the offending cloak right across Claudia's feet. Himself he flung into a chair and swore as he should not have sworn in the presence of his wife. Claudia picked up the cloak between finger and thumb, cast it from her, and told him what she thought of him. Lucius in his rage at some evil that had happened, and Claudia in her anger at his boorish ways, had quite forgotten Iras. She sat in her dark corner and listened with all her ears, while her skin prickled and her blood ran cold.

"... every child under two years old, in Bethlehem and the country round, to be murdered," Lucius was muttering furiously. "These are the orders of that foul beast Herod. And why? Because he's heard some old wives' tale that a king has been born in Bethlehem who shall be greater than he. Nothing but a fairy tale told him by some crazy madmen from the desert. The man's insane."

Claudia sat up and swung her feet to the floor. She looked sick and shaken. "When?" she asked.

"To-night," said Lucius grimly. "He will send his own assassins, I thank the gods. He will not require my co-operation."

"But you'll not permit it?" she whispered.

Lucius shrugged his shoulders. "Herod is the ruler of this province, and I am under his orders," he said. "And those orders do not permit of interference."

Iras put a hand over her mouth to stifle a cry. The Centurion Lucius was not a bad man; he loved his wife and he was kinder to the slaves than Claudia was; Iras would never forget how kind he had been the night her father had been killed. Yet he would stand aside and permit this horrible thing, just because those were his orders. How could he? She looked at him, at his set hard mouth, his brooding eyes, his heavy figure slumped almost despairingly in his chair, and realized something of the dreadfulness of the military machine of which he was a part. It had conquered nearly the whole world now, and it had done that because of this iron discipline that drove men like Lucius, naturally kindly men, to countenance deeds of unspeakable horror rather than fail in obedience to a superior officer. . . . And Herod was not even a Roman. He was a native of this little country who had chosen to throw in his lot with her conquerors that he might not lose his own poor pomp and state. He was a despicable creature who would stick at nothing, it seemed, to remain a king; not even at mass murder. . . . Abruptly Iras ceased thinking of him for she had remembered Mary and her baby. Quick as thought she got up and crept through the shadows to the door. The last thing she saw was Claudia kneeling at her husband's feet, clasping his knees, weeping, pleading. But there was no time to wait for a possible but unlikely yielding. . . . No time. . . . No time.

It was quite dark as she ran out of the villa, and the great stars were bright already in the sky. She ran down through the olive groves to the road, alone in the night, but she forgot to be afraid, for her thoughts were entirely occupied with Mary and the baby, and as she ran she thought what she should do. It would be best, she thought, not to tell Joseph and Mary that other babies besides their own were threatened, for in trying to warn others they might delay their own departure until too late. Instinctively she knew that no worse tragedy could befall the world than that their baby should not grow into a man. She would do what she could, herself, after she had warned Mary and Joseph, to save the others. . . . And perhaps Claudia would succeed in her pleading. Perhaps Lucius would restrain those wicked men. There was still hope.

She reached the gates of Bethlehem and to her great relief they were still unlocked. She ran up the steep starlit streets until she reached the shop, and looking up saw Joseph sitting at the top of the steps, his cloak wrapped about him, his head sunk on his breast.

"Joseph! Joseph!" she cried, and ran up the steps.

He lifted his head and looked at her. His kind dark eyes were worried and puzzled in his wrinkled, grey-bearded face. He had dreamed a confused yet dreadful dream of swords flashing against a night sky, of the screaming of a woman and the wailing of a child. Awakening from it he had stumbled out into the fresh air and sat down at the top of the steps. He was still drowsy when the sound of footsteps and the crying of his name made him lift his head from his chest.

"Joseph! Take Mary and the baby and fly! King Herod will kill your child. Quickly, Joseph, quickly!" She fell upon him, shaking him almost savagely. "Wake up, Joseph, wake up! What I tell you is true. I heard it from the Centurion Lucius. Herod fears your child. He has heard how the great men from the East came to worship him."

Father Abraham! It was the little Egyptian slave! Joseph was fully awake and on his feet in a moment. She was a brave, sensible little maid, and with the influence of his dream strong upon him he did not doubt that what she said was true. He knew King Herod to be a man so evil as to be almost insane, his hatred of those who threatened his power a thing abnormal. The intention Iras ascribed to him was in keeping with his twisted nature. He did not question Iras further, he only demanded of her: "Where, Iras, where? Home to Nazareth? With Mary stronger we should have gone back in any case."

"No, no, right away out of the country!" cried Iras passionately. "Across the frontier, where Herod can't get at you." Like a vision against the night she could see her home, mountain-built with peaceful citadel, with about it the orange groves, the date palms, the clover field and the wells of sweet water, and beyond, the glorious golden sand of the desert. "Egypt," she said, "and I will guide you."

"It's a long way," said Joseph, "and you a little maid when you travelled it last."

"I shall do it," she said. And she did not doubt that from

somewhere, somehow, the power would come. During the three years that were passed, when the idea of trying to escape back home had occurred to her, she had thrust it away as a thing impossible. But she was older now and the sense of something at stake greater than she could understand aroused in her a daring that matched it in greatness. She became at once the leader of this desperate expedition.

"Mary cannot walk all the way," she said. "Go you, Joseph, and find a donkey. Buy it, borrow it, steal it even. I will wake Mary."

He went off noiselessly into the night and she went in and awakened Mary. Together they put together in bundles the things they would need; food, water-bottles that Iras filled at the well behind the house, the baby's little clothes, and their few treasures. Mary, faced by the dreadful danger and by the hazardous journey into an unknown land, was brave and serene. She worked quickly but without panic. "Be it unto me according to Thy word" was all the prayer that she had time for. When their packing was finished they took the baby out of his cradle and wrapped him in his little striped blanket. He whimpered a little, roused so suddenly from his sleep, but held in his mother's arms, warm against her warm body, he was soon asleep again.

Leaving Mary crooning to him, Iras crept outside. Now was her chance, before Joseph returned, to warn those other mothers. She ran down the steps and looked up the street; and saw Joseph coming down towards her with the donkey. He saw her, waved, and came on more urgently. No time was left. A terrible distress seized Iras. Her knees trembled beneath her and she had to sit down on the steps, sick and faint with horror. The world seemed to go black about her, and then Joseph was bending over, shaking her as earlier in the night she had shaken him. "No time for weakness now," he said. "Fetch Mary. Make haste."

They set out through the quiet streets, Mary sitting on the

donkey with the baby in her arms, the bundles strapped behind her. The gate of the city was still unbarred, and they passed through into the deep stillness of the country beyond. So peaceful was it that in spite of that ominously unbarred gate Iras was visited by the wild hope that Claudia had been successful in her beseeching, and that Lucius had turned back the murderers. But even as the hope was born it died for there came the sound of horses' hoofs in the distance, and a sharp command that cut the still air like a whiplash. Joseph led the donkey off the road into the darkness of the olive groves and with beating hearts they watched the troop go by; Herod's own men, wearing his colours, armoured and fine under the starlight, yet silent, with something of his own evil in their faces and his own despair in their hearts, the pitiful creatures of a will that was not their own.

"Poor souls!" cried Mary, pitying this most desperate of all human plights.

And Iras, crouching, shivering with hands over her face, echoed the cry deep in her heart; but she was not thinking of Herod's soldiers, or even of Lucius who had not after all been persuaded, but of the mothers of Bethlehem and their children. Could she be forgiven that she had not dared to wait and warn them? Was it possible that somehow, somewhere, they would forgive her? She could see no hope of forgiveness. She must carry the burden of this horror until she died.

They went on, and Iras saw to it that they travelled so fast that no sound reached them from the little town they left behind.

V

Till the day of her death Iras did not forget that adventurous journey to the land of Egypt. When she thought of it as an old woman she thought of it as a symbol of all journeys and all adventures, especially of that most arduous journey from birth to death that we call life. Every terrifying aspect of adventurous living was present in that journey; danger, hardship, pain, anxiety, and even, at times, despair. The sun burned them by day and the cold froze them by night. They were footsore and exhausted, hungry and thirsty, and the sun and stars were their only guides to that far-away, almost mythical city that their straining eyes saw sometimes as a mirage in the distance but their stumbling feet could never reach. They were always in danger, from thieves, from their own despair that tempted them sometimes to lie down, give up the struggle and hold out their arms to the beneficence of death.

Yet there was a splendour over all that journey. As each torment met them there leaped out to confront it Mary's gay courage, Joseph's patient strength, Iras's determined endurance, and those things seemed always greater than the danger and the pain. This is what God is, thought Iras, a voice that answers always more mightily than the voice that challenges, a perpetual assurance that the final end is good. . . . Above all there was the baby, the reason for it all, the centre of their living and their striving, their joy, their pride, their home. That upper room where his cradle had been had been home. Wherever, now, they made his bed in the twilight, that was home too. That city on the hill towards which they journeyed, and where he would rest in safety, that would be home again. He would be the end of it all, for he had been the beginning, he was the now and always that made the two things one.

Yet no victory over weakness or despair was ever as yet the final victory; they came back again and again, and especially to Iras, who was so young and who must bear the agony of Bethlehem with her now wherever she went. At night she would lie staring into the darkness, wondering if she had done right, trying to think what other course she could have taken, sickened like thousands before and after her at the terrible mesh of evil that held the guilty and innocent together in such a stranglehold that scarcely a soul could escape without taint;

wondering above all if it were possible that somehow, somewhere, those mothers and children would forgive her. Such pain as hers cannot continue. It must reach its height at last and break one way or the other into madness or relief. And it broke with Iras on the night when the stars were hidden.

When they lay down that night they knew that they were lost. They were in Egypt now, and safe from King Herod, but they did not know how to find Iras's home. She knew only that it was to the eastward, and towards the east they had travelled for days and seen nothing but the golden sand of the desert, the burning sky by day and the stars by night. They had met no caravans from whom they could have enquired the way. Nothing. Fear was upon them as never before.

And now, tonight, the heavens were clouded and the stars were hidden. A storm must have passed close by, leaving this strange grey veil over the sky. They could not even know where the east was. Mary and Joseph, worn out, were sleeping in spite of their fear, but Iras was at the breaking point. While memory was hers, she thought, she would never sleep again.

Self-tortured, she could not lie still. She crept over to where the baby lay in the cradle hollowed out of the sand and crouched beside him, looking intently at the tiny sleeping face that she could scarcely see in the darkness. Will you die too? she wondered. Was Bethlehem's agony all for nothing? She rocked backwards and forwards in her grief, but silently, lest she woke him. She had been so certain that this life must be saved at all costs, yet had not the price been too high, for what could he do for the world, this peasant's child whose life was opening in exile and poverty, with evil men seeking his life? With such a beginning, what could the end be except the closing in of the pursuers and the hounding down of the prey? She bowed down upon herself, and wept. All the suffering of the poor men, the exiles, the persecuted, from the beginning of the world until this moment, and from this moment on until the end, seemed with her in this abysmal hour. From the beginning and from the end flowed the two streams of sorrow, converging about this cradle in the desert where the baby slept so peacefully. He always slept peacefully wherever he was. He was as much at home here in the heart of sorrow as he had been in the happiness of Bethlehem.

Suddenly, beside her in the night, she heard the small cheerful sound which a baby makes when it awakes and looks out upon some sight which seems to it good, a sound rather like the cry of a bird in the dawn, a crowing contented sound full of satisfaction. She opened her eyes and looked about her, and so soft and radiant was the light that at first she thought that the moon and the stars must have pierced the veil of cloud and be shining again. But the sky was as dark as ever. It was from the desert itself that the light came, from a circle of brightness that shone all round them and radiated from the laughing faces and the shining garments of a multitude of little children, gathered about them as though in protection. She gasped and rubbed her eyes, and looked again, but they were still there, angel children, not of this world, yet retaining the humanity of their laughter, and with their mothers' love about them still, a nimbus of glory about each shining head. They were like stars in the night, like the flowers of Paradise whose perfume was all about them; virgin lilies and the roses of martyrdom, and all the homely flowers whose scent is as the breath of home to every exile under the sun. Crying aloud in her joy, Iras stretched out her arms to the children. But they could not come to her arms, for they were not of her world; yet the light that was about them pierced right through to her soul and wrapped about with their forgiveness, as with a shining cloak, she lay down and slept.

She awoke as the first gleam of dawn was silvering the clouded sky, and nothing was changed; there was no break in the clouds to show where the sun was rising, they were still hungry and footsore and lost in the desert; yet her despair had gone, for with her own eyes she had seen those angel children encamped about them, and her sense of safety made her feel as at home now in the heart of sorrow as the babe himself.

She awakened Mary and Joseph and they ate the last of their dates and drank a very little water from the water-bottle. Then Mary gave suck to the child while Iras and Joseph rolled up their bundles and strapped them to the donkey's back. They spoke very little, and their faces were pallid in the dim light, yet their few words were spoken cheerfully. "If this is the end," said Mary, "I shall not curse God as I die, for I have most surely known Him upon this journey; I have held Him in my arms in the body of my child, seen Him in the bright sun and heard His voice in the wind, felt His love in my heart and His courage in my soul. Even in hell I will remember, and my soul will magnify the Lord."

And Joseph said, "Amen."

Then he and Iras lifted Mary and her baby upon the donkey's back and they set out walking they knew not where, stumbling with fatigue, their faces set towards the place where Iras imagined that the sky was brightest. That was the only guide they had now; Iras's fancy that just there the sun was rising.

Late in the day they halted, and drank the very last of the water, and Mary lay down with the babe in her arms and slept. Even Joseph, sitting with head sunk on his breast, dozed a little for very weariness. Iras left them and went a little way off by herself. Where was that outcrop of rock in the desert that had been her home? There was nothing in the great expanse of the shrouded sky and the rolling desert that could help her, no landmark that she could recognize. They had drunk the last of the water and nothing lay before them now but an unspeakably dreadful death. Yet she was not afraid because she knew that the angel children were round about them, she only wondered what one ought to do when one got to the end. Then she remembered what Mary had said that morning, "Even in hell my soul will magnify the Lord." That one could do. One could praise God from Whom came all things and to Whom all things returned, the One God of the Pharaoh Aknaton, the Alpha and Omega of the Hebrews, the beginning and the end, the God Whose answer was always greater than any challenge, even the final challenge of death. She knelt down and worshipped, as the Eastern people worship, her forehead bent low to the ground, her hands outstretched. And as she whispered broken words of praise and adoration she sank lower in her weakness until she was lying face downward, and thus she lay for a long time, only half conscious, her hands fumbling the sand as a child's fingers grope at its mother's breast. And then, as consciousness returned, she found that her fingers had touched something hidden under the sand. She sat up and looked at it; a little withered bunch of orange blossom, such as she remembered growing in pots in the window of her home. She held the flowers to her face and breathed the faint scent of them; it was familiar not only from the happy past but from the vision of last night, for its scent had mingled, she remembered, with the scent of the virgin lilies and the roses of martyrdom. She bent her forehead to the ground and again praised God.

Then she went back to Mary and Joseph and showed them what she had found. "Look," she said, "flowers of Paradise. Angel children, going home, have dropped them to show us the way."

And Mary held out her hands for the flowers with the speechless longing of those to whom death seems now the only good.

But Joseph accepted no such fanciful explanation of the phenomenon. He went quickly to the place where Iras had found the flowers and began to clear away the soft blown sand. "A caravan has passed this way," he said. "The storm that clouded the sky has blown fresh sand over the tracks. Look, Iras, a little broken pot. And camels' spoor, and in the harder sand a place where water has been spilt."

Their deathly weariness vanished as though it had never been. They went forward again quickly and eagerly, refreshed like children awakened out of sleep, and suddenly they were beyond the path of the storm and the tracks of a recent caravan were clear and easy to follow.

"The clouds are breaking," said Mary, and she did not speak in allegory but with literal truth. The strange ominous haze was thinning, lightening, rolling back like a scroll to show a glorious clear patch of golden sky, and blocked before it, towering up into the streaming light, far off but clear and distinct at the end of the track that they followed, was a city built upon a hill.

There would never be a joy like this again for Iras, not until the final journey home that would take her beyond the gates of death. Nearer and nearer came the familiar outline of the beloved city, with the cool greenness of the date palms flung about it, and the orange groves and the fields of clover. Presently she fancied she could see the very house that was her home. The pots of orange blossom would be standing in the window and behind them her mother would be sitting at her loom.

"It is built into the rock, like Bethlehem," said Mary wistfully.

"All the world over hill towns are like each other," said Joseph. "That will ease the homesickness." He turned and smiled at Mary, walking beside him now, for it was Iras's turn to ride upon the donkey with the baby in her arms. "Remember, Mary, that it is always by the waters of Babylon that our people sing their songs. Our son would be no true son of his people if he did not taste of that pain also. But one day, at long last, we shall go home. Every exile has its ending."

In spite of her joy a sword pierced suddenly through Iras's heart as she looked down at the baby in her arms. How would she live when he went away again? Then she remembered how in the agony of the night that was passed she had found him in the centre of it. In the years that were coming she would grow to be an old woman in her land, and he would grow to manhood in his land, and the desert would lie between. Yet in that she would find him, and where he was would be sorrow, also home.

(*Reproduced from "The Ikon on the Wall," Gerald Duckworth*)

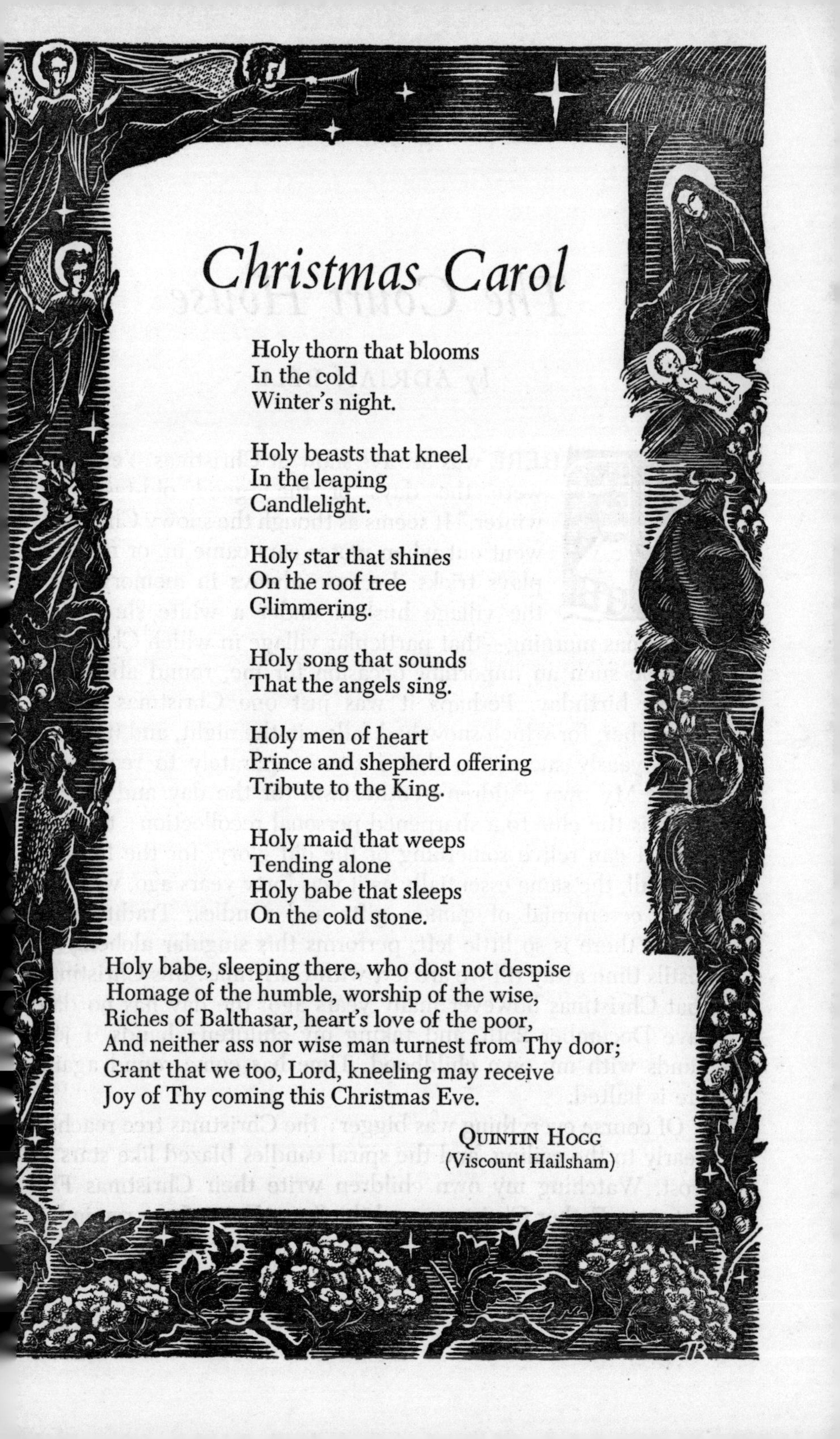

Christmas Carol

Holy thorn that blooms
In the cold
Winter's night.

Holy beasts that kneel
In the leaping
Candlelight.

Holy star that shines
On the roof tree
Glimmering.

Holy song that sounds
That the angels sing.

Holy men of heart
Prince and shepherd offering
Tribute to the King.

Holy maid that weeps
Tending alone
Holy babe that sleeps
On the cold stone.

Holy babe, sleeping there, who dost not despise
Homage of the humble, worship of the wise,
Riches of Balthasar, heart's love of the poor,
And neither ass nor wise man turnest from Thy door;
Grant that we too, Lord, kneeling may receive
Joy of Thy coming this Christmas Eve.

QUINTIN HOGG
(Viscount Hailsham)

The Court House

by ADRIAN BELL

HERE was always snow at Christmas. Yes, those were the days of the "good old-fashioned winter." It seems as though the snowy Christmas went out when motor cars came in, or memory plays tricks; because always in memory I see the village hushed under a white shroud on Christmas morning—that particular village in which Christmas became such an important occasion for me, round about my eighth birthday. Perhaps it was just one Christmas Day I remember, for which snow had fallen in the night, and it stands for a yearly succession that I seem separately to recall and enjoy. My own children's enthusiasm for the day and for the snow is the clue to a sharpened personal recollection: through them I can relive something of the old glory; for the feast is, after all, the same essentially as it was forty years ago, with the same ceremonial of games, gifts and candles. Tradition, of which there is so little left, performs this singular alchemy; it distils time away till we are left with Christmas; this Christmas, that Christmas however many years ago; the day has no date save December 25th, and taking my children's hands, I join hands with my own childhood. Time has come round again: life is halted.

Of course everything was bigger: the Christmas tree reached nearly to the ceiling, and the spiral candles blazed like stars in frost. Watching my own children write their Christmas Eve letters to Father Christmas and the Snow Fairy, I am reminded of the nursery mythology which was so cogent a part of our environment. At Christmas it was the very air we breathed. In those days nobody questioned the right of children to whole galaxies of fairies. I always suspect the grown-ups indulged themselves too (in a way that psychologists would nowadays explain) in populating our minds with these miraculous folk: they read us fairy tales by the fire; they made them up for us on walks. We had all Grimm and Hans Andersen: learned professors and mathematicians were heart and soul in it too: we wished the rainbow a more extended range, that there might be yet another coloured Fairy Book by Andrew Lang: and of course we knew the Knave of Hearts before we saw him on a playing card. With all this, yes, it was a heavenly time. There were a few bogies, to be sure, that might pop up in dark places; and a certain two-headed giant I found particularly repellent; but luckily he was at the end of the book, so I was certain, so long as I did not explore beyond page 292 that I should not be confronted by him. The benign spirits were the reigning influences, our parents saw to that, despite superstitious country nursemaids.

Of course the bogies were not all imaginary. I blundered into a bedroom one morning and saw my uncle's head resting upon a box. It seems he had bought a kind of patent Turkish bath for home use and was sweating off some obesity inside it. But a human head with a box for body was all I saw.

That village was steep and stone-walled. The houses formed a hollow square, facing outward; and the hollow square was filled with orchards, and in the orchards were the cottagers' and the gentlefolk's cows, the Major's pigs and Hannah Cook's sow and Charlie Weston's geese, a sprinkling of sheep, a grey horse, cocks and hens. In spring they lived under blossom through bee-loud days: in summer they lay shady in their green closes. In winter they stayed in sties and byres and bartons. Big house, little house, pigsty, barn—all were built to the same plain gracious pattern in Cotswold stone.

To me it was a place of first encounters. Cock-crow I heard

for the first time there. What a wonderful hullabaloo that was, breaking out of the shades of night. It was the first thing that told me, in the blank minute of awakening, that I was mysteriously somewhere new, somewhere different from yesterday. Yesterday there had been the by-no-means unmelodious sounds of a London street: the jingle of a hansom, a cry of "Any coal?" (Think of it, shivering in the mid-twentieth century, coal actually being hawked!), and the muffin-man's bell. But now a strange silence, a thickened stillness, and "cockadoodledoo!" ripping suddenly through it, followed by a listening pause, then "cockadoodledoo!" sounding distantly, yet more distantly; then suddenly close and loud again. First impressions must be enduring, for whenever I hear that sound breaking out of darkness, even today, I have for a moment that feeling of unlimited hope and freshness, as though I were about to step forth into an England echoing to the horns of chivalry. There was indeed not a little pageantry remaining to English country life even in the days of my childhood, from the vestments of the clergyman on such a day as this, to the puffed-up, glistening, multi-coloured cocks of random breed which had their little kingdoms in those orchards. The mummers who performed by candlelight in my aunt's great kitchen had, I remember, their own bizarre attire; even the village pumps, swathed and hooded now in straw, looked like mummers.

The first wonder of Christmas Day was the absolute perfection of that snow. I spent some time studying the footprints of birds and vermin in it, and observing how it had built itself up to a height of several inches on every ledge and branch; how it capped the nose of a garden statue, and filled his outstretched hand with a cold, pure gift. The evergreens hung heavy with great white aprons of snow; the swing suspended from the apple tree bore an oblong brick of it. A stillness was on everything, broken only by a sudden cascade from some overburdened bough, which spilled itself in a great sigh and startled me, leaving a white spume in the air.

Presently the snow-plough came past: it was drawn by a grey horse treading silently, rather a ghostly figure: a driver so heavily wrapped as to be hardly human stood on the apex of the plough. On this particular morning I had permission to ride a little way on the plough; a very exciting experience, almost equal to imaginary rides with Santa Claus on his sledge, with the snow foaming and hissing past me as it was pushed into a pile on either side. Being so close to the ground, by watching it I had the illusion of travelling at breathless speed, and it was a surprise to look up and see the horse trudging so steadily. Getting off at the corner where the shop was, as I had been told to do, I stood and watched the snow-plough departing, with an envy of the giant toys with which grown-ups beguiled their days.

The shop provided practically everything the village required beyond the home produce, pickled and preserved by family recipe, which lined the ample larders, store-cupboards and cellars of the houses. The small community could have withstood a siege by snow of many weeks' duration.

One is fortunate to have so happy a first impression. I thought it was the most beautiful place in the world: it is for me, at any rate, the most beautiful place in time. It is the point at which imagination and reality meet, as sometimes sea and sky seem to mingle on a luminous horizon. Luckily I am as proportionately far removed from it in distance as I am in years. The country of my manhood has been wide open, windy, toilsome, hard; demanding a life of action. The pageantry of its corn has been intrinsic with the unresting muscular quality of its arable farming. That country, however, of my childhood was bosky, and had more of a pastoral, peasant quality. The only actual visible pledges of it I have are a few water-colours done by a lady resident in the village at that time; and in them I revisit those very scenes as I saw them. The eyes of the artist must be as perceptive as the eyes of the child: the cottages in Cow Lane have that same living quality in the water-colour as they had for me.

The sudden dip of the lane leads the eye into imaginary fields by willow brooks, in which fields I actually walked and picked flowers. There were a few lamps—one, I think, at each corner of the village. None of the lamp-posts stood straight: my artist has pictured the one at the corner of Cow Lane at just the right eloquent angle; eloquent of what I could not say, but by no means just a lamp-post that required setting upright, which is all my adult eye would have observed. She saw, as I saw then, how the angle of the lamp entered into the spirit of Cow Lane. Similarly, the lamp at the edge of the Common, where the village ended in a wild garden of gorse, had its own stiff gesture, as of a torch thrust forward to glimmer into the twilight of that waste. That was a sunset country, in which the sky, even as she has painted it, was full of incident at evening.

It was near this spot that I first encountered the good ladies who lived in the Court House, one of whom painted the water-colours. The encounter took place, I seem to feel, on this very Christmas morning, not long after I had reluctantly quitted the snow-plough. The sight of two boys snowballing had led me along this road, instead of turning back homeward as I had been instructed. The temptation to witness at closer range that battle of white blobs bursting on caps and shoulders got the better of me. I stood staring: this obviously was the greatest fun in the world. Suddenly everything became very cold and wet and suffocating, as one of the snowballs burst against my own face. I was startled, but swiftly recovered, and joined in the game. The next thing that happened was a furious yelping, and a sharp pain in my seat. I yelped too: the two boys shouted, and two female voices seemed to be crying out both angrily and sympathetically at the same time. Next moment, one of the Misses Calver had me in her arms, and her sister their dog by the collar. I heard somebody scolding, "You're very, very naughty"; which I knew I was, to have come that way, and I sobbed bitterly. But she who had me folded in her arms was saying, "My poor little man, does it hurt? Never mind, we'll soon make it better." I had forgotten whether it hurt or where, but stopped still, to try and make out what really had happened. I saw then to my relief that it was the dog whom Miss Rosa was calling "very, very naughty"; a hideous animal showing the whites of his eyes and the whole range of his teeth. What made the scene a little unreal was the fact that she had in her left hand a butterfly net (presumably the first thing she had picked up) with which she was endeavouring to belabour the dog at each reiteration of the word "very." An unsatisfactory implement, as the dog's claws kept catching in the netting. Finally he got it over his head, and plunged free, carrying it away with him through the house with a tremendous rattling. This rather pleased me: but then, looking down I saw a single drop of blood on the snow, dreadful and dramatic. I traced its source to a thin runnel of blood down my leg, realized then that the naughtiness of the dog was in having nipped me in the pants, and started to howl in earnest.

Next minute I was staring at the pattern of a carpet which had red, ragged designs and colourful crookednesses, amid which occurred a number of little brown holes. I had a very close view of the carpet, as I was more or less upside down, having the bite on my bottom examined by the two ladies and their maid. The maid seemed to have taken charge of the proceedings: those were the days when country maids were often persons of maturity and resource. The wound, I was assured, was nothing, just a tiny nip. "Oh that naughty Bobby—I really will beat him for it," cried Miss Rosa at sight of the teeth-marks, and rushed off as though to perform the chastisement effectually this time. What was worrying me was not the extent of the damage, but a picture that had sprung into my mind's eye as I gazed at the Oriental contortions in the carpet before my face. It was a picture that my nurse had planted there, a simple good lass of this village. She once told me how a certain blacksmith—she named the very village in which it had occurred—as he plied his trade at his open forge, was bitten by a mad dog. He was a very powerful man, and told his friends to bind him with the strongest cords while there was yet time. This they did, and before long he began to struggle and foam at the mouth. He strained at the cords in dreadful spasms, and if free would no doubt have dashed himself and his friends to death. But the bonds held, and after a time the frenzy passed away, leaving him weak but in his right mind.

That was the stirring kind of tale our nurses used to tell us on afternoon walks. The mad dog was a prominent bogey of those days. Now the horrid picture forced itself into my mind; and I wondered, ought I to ask these ladies to bind me up with strong cords? I could only falter out, upside down as I was, in a most unheroic attitude, "Please, Miss Calver—is your dog mad?"

"Bless you dear, no: it was just that he thought you were attacking him with those snowballs I expect. Mad—oh, no."

She and her Agnes laughed at the idea: the dressing of the tender spot was done, and I was sat right way up. I found myself on a large sofa with a large cat on each arm of it, and Miss Rosa entering the room with a glass of milk and a slice of chocolate cake on a plate.

Much relieved that the dog was bad, not mad, I ate the cake and stared at the room. Wherever you might have expected a vase to be, or a clock, was a cat. There were a great many cats. Even things that did not look like cats, but like muffs, or tippets, or footstools, in time uncurled and became cats. I believed that if I had stared at the copper warming-pan for long enough, that too would have become a cat; it had lively reflections of them. I was sitting in front of a fireplace so big it reminded me of the church porch: there were stone faces carved on the mantel. On the hearth blazed a great log. A log? It was *the* log, it has become the Yule Log of all time to me. We had descended one or two steps into the room, which would have been dim but for the light of the fire. The walls were rather rough, as though whitewashed directly over the stone.

I had finished the cake, and was just drinking the milk, when the equilibrium of the firebrands gave way, and the log bumped down off the dogs and rolled out towards the room with a golden shower of sparks bursting from the point of impact. Embers like so many red imps leaped on to the carpet.

"Oh, dear," "Rosa," "Jean," "Agnes," various voices cried. Cats spat and hissed and leaped on to window-sills and tops of cupboards. With a yelp, a dog—yes, it was *the* dog who had crept back and hidden under the sofa—fled, buffeting a china cupboard, while the sisters did a stamping, shuffling dance, in which Agnes joined them, extinguishing the embers. That done, the great log was levered back into position with the fire-irons. The little brown holes in the carpet were explained.

With a mingled odour of hot milk, scorching fur and chocolate cake about me I went upstairs with Miss Jean while she prepared herself for church. The stairs were broad and oaken, and on our way up Miss Jean, who had a funny little sideways twist to her head, told me how Jake, the gardener-handyman, had said to her (and her voice imitated Jake's, as though she were screwing the words out of her throat), "When the old Captain lived here, he told me I was to polish these here stairs every Saturday. That I did till they shone like glass, and one day the Captain fell from top to bottom with a basket of apples. After that he told me not to polish 'em no more, and I was glad."

Miss Jean's was a room of the same dimensions as the one we had left; but the walls were panelled and there was some emblazonry on the window glass. She went to the wall, and behold, three of the panels moved and became a door, and opened on to a small winding stairway. "There's supposed to be a secret passage," she said mysteriously, "between this house and the rectory, under the ground."

This thrilled me. "Can we explore?" I had long wished to gain entry to this house, because of things my nurse Lucy had told me about it. Its name, "The Court House," was as inviting as the title page of a fairy tale. And here I was, in nobody's charge either, for Miss Jean treated me simply as a friend. One's own grown-ups were always so proprietary, with their "don'ts" and "come along now," as though one's function were simply not to do them discredit. That nip in the seat had really been providential.

One of my most thrilling occupations as a child was to explore a house, particularly an old house, a house with a story. That this was a very mysterious house, I felt at once. Children, of all ages, have a keen nose for atmosphere. But it was a friendly house, I felt that; in spite of what Lucy had told me about things being mysteriously thrown about in it, and people not being able to stay long. That Captain had come a cropper, certainly. I had an instinct to keep within the radius of Miss Jean's voice and presence; she guaranteed the harmlessness: no, more than that, she turned something that might have been baneful even to blessedness.

"The passage has been blocked up and hidden; but we *will* explore when you come again."

"But how do you know there was a passage?"

She had on her hat and coat, and picked up her prayer book from beside her bed. "Because," she said quite simply, pointing with the prayer book in her hand to the panelled secret door, "every night of a festival day such as today, at about twelve o'clock, a procession of choirboys comes through that door with lighted candles in their hands, singing very sweetly, and they go across the room and out through that other door to the landing." She began to murmur a few notes of music.

"Do you mean—you see them?" I asked eagerly.

"See them? I should think I do. They rather keep me awake, you know. I tell them: 'I like your singing, but I'm so sleepy would you mind not coming through my bedroom?' But they take no notice."

I stared. "Anything else—I mean, do you see anybody else?"

"Why, yes—there are two little pages in blue velvet, not much bigger than you. Dear little boys, and such a pretty blue, their suits. Occasionally I come upon them playing on the landing."

"Do you——? And when you see them, are you——?" I couldn't somehow say the word "frightened."

She laughed so gaily as we crossed the landing as was answer enough. I looked round hopefully, but saw no pages. "Oh, I like company," she said.

Miss Rosa was waiting in the hall. She had a round, kind, ordinary sort of face; she, I thought, might well have been a mother, and made nice cakes and told you what to do and what not to do. Miss Jean, I saw, was somewhere beyond cakes and behaviour. I was glad Miss Rosa was there, to look after the cakes side of things. But Miss Jean really *understood.*

I was a little stiff at first, but I soon forgot about that as I walked holding Miss Jean's hand. I felt I had a great deal to say to her: she and her house were right inside my secret world. Yet because I was so brimful of queries that were but disguised recognitions, I could not break the silence that seemed to express them all.

What really held me silent was the sense of the difference between Lucy and Miss Jean as regards those "goings on." It was Lucy who first had breathed of them, but in fearful low-toned references, as of one who must every now and again be jerking aside a curtain to peep at something she did not want to see. But now it made by contrast a sort of brightness in me that Miss Jean simply welcomed these visitants as she had welcomed me. I had been told, you see, that she "saw things," but had had no idea that she saw them—so simply.

I asked Miss Rosa, I remember, if she saw the pages; more I think to make conversation than anything else.

"Well—no, I can't exactly say that I see them—but sometimes I hear . . ." She broke off with "But I don't know that we ought to give you ideas that might——" She looked to her sister, bewildered to know whether I ought or oughtn't at my age to have an idea that might——

I reassured her, that I should have loved to see them. Holding Miss Jean's hand, I certainly should.

I gazed up into the clear sky joyfully. Just then the silence of the snow and sky was filled with the clang of the single last bell of the church. It was as the mellow boom of a gong that was the circle of the sky itself. Miss Jean was looking up too, drinking in the great sound.

Boom—boom. Miss Rosa hurried on ahead, as our pace was slow. Miss Jean showed no desire to hurry me. We walked on together unspeaking, in the beauty of this great bell. We stopped a moment, where a yew-tree's trunk showed a bright powdery green of lichen against the snow. The bell seemed to show it to us. We came to the dripping well in the wall. It was a kind of grotto, sprouting ferns, with water from some hidden spring oozing down the rocks and a square basin of stone slabs below which conserved it. We stopped at this wonder of water flowing in frost as at the shrine of a miracle which the great bell celebrated. The movement of the dripping just kept the surface from freezing: we stared at pebbles brilliant in the limpid depths. Very much I wanted to drink some of the water. I have never lost the desire to drink from a spring in passing. Surprisingly—yet not surprisingly—Miss Jean did not say "No, not now; come along, hurry up," but waited while I knelt with cupped hands to the pool.

We passed the Home Farm, where the dairy door stood open showing great shallow pans of milk, let into the slabs that were built on round stone pillars. I do not know of what material the pans were made—I only remember the smooth perfection of square lakes of milk set in stone. The bell boomed more slowly.

Now we had reached my aunt's house, from which I had set out that morning on the snow-plough. I was handed in there, with apologies and explanations. But I was not done with my guide yet, even if she was prepared for the present to relinquish me. There was one question uppermost in my mind which I had been wanting to put to her. Once or twice I had been on the point of it: that was specifically what I had stopped for, at the tree and at the well. But somehow I could not quite summon up the courage to ask outright on either occasion. Yet she seemed somehow to have been awaiting just such a question. For Lucy had told me—and this was said to account in high measure for Miss Jean's "queerness," but to me now knowing her, it was the source of her luminous simplicity—that she had once seen "an angel." This information had originated in Agnes, who had had it, it was rumoured, from Miss Jean herself. An angel had stood beside her in the church, so close that she had felt the brush of the wings. Again, Miss Rosa had failed to substantiate the presence, yet would not go so far as to say that there had been absolutely nothing there. It had been during "sung Eucharist." Whatever that might be I did not enquire.

But I tremendously wanted to know, from her own lips, whether she had actually seen, and touched, an angel. I wanted to know too, very much, about the wings.

I begged to be allowed to go on with her now, as far as the church. It was only a few hundred yards: my request was granted. The great bell had ceased: we walked in the resumed and utter calm of the snow. When we reached the churchyard; then, I felt, would be the moment for my question.

We passed under the lych-gate. "You must come and have tea with me," Miss Jean was saying. "Tell Lucy to bring you soon."

"Lucy?" I questioned. Her presence would spoil everything, the whole blessed joy of the place.

"She is a friend of Agnes—they can have tea together. And then just you and I can explore." It had become to me even more than the house that we should explore.

But my all-important question. We were half-way to the porch.

"Miss Jean," I blurted out, "did you . . . ?" She turned at the porch. "Yes?" The organ was trumpeting within.

"Did you really, once, see——?"

She smiled on me, such a smile; and bent and kissed me, and then she was gone.

I returned to the house slowly, kicking up the snow as I went, dissatisfied that after all I had not quite managed it. It seemed immensely important to know. But just as I turned in at the gates of the drive I realized that it did not matter that I had not quite put the question. I realized that I did know.

In My Opinion

by GODFREY WINN

I DID not know what loneliness really meant, what being alone could do to the human spirit, until I found myself plonked down in New York, a few days before Christmas some years ago. I sat in my over-heated, luxurious bedroom in my Fifth Avenue hotel, waiting for the telephone to ring, and longing with all my heart to be back at home, whatever degree of austerity that entailed in regard to material things.

It was my first visit to America, on a lecture tour, and I knew no one. For Christmas, I had banked entirely on two friends of mine, who were to be staying in the same hotel, and had promised to look after me. Alas, both of them, in one fell swoop, were stricken down by the influenza germ that is no respecter of riches, more powerful even than the armour of central heating. I felt lost and hopeless, and cursed the fact that it was Christmas, with its nostalgic impingement upon my defence mechanism. I longed to be out on the road, speaking and barnstorming. I longed for Christmas to be over, and the job to begin, of trying to present a picture of a stricken Europe, still in a state of siege. The opulence of Christmas in New York was savagely at variance with the pictures that crowded my mind. And I began to wish that I had never set out on this new adventure.

That was the mood I was in, when at last the telephone did ring, and I received my first invitation: to broadcast, on Christmas Eve, over the Columbia network. A crisp, feminine voice said: "We have a programme called 'In My Opinion.' Each time we have two speakers expressing entirely divergent points of view. This week, considering the season, we thought it would be topical, if we took as our subject for debate 'Fairy Tales, or Reality?' For children, I mean. Does the idea appeal to you? Would you like to speak on one side or the other? And if so, which side?"

There was a pause, I hesitated, and then I said: "You mean, should children be encouraged to believe in Father Christmas, in this age of the Atom Bomb?" "Exactly." There was another pause, and then I heard myself say: "Well, I think I would like to stand up for Father Christmas. I mean, he has such a raw deal these days, and it must be very disheartening for him, struggling to get his sleigh over the top of the Empire State Building."

I broke off, thinking that sounded "whimsy," which, heaven knows, was the last thing I had come to America to be. But the crisp, executive voice the other end seemed delighted. "Splendid! We have a lady who is the head of a child guidance clinic who is *very* anxious to take the opposite view. So that should make a good debate. May I have your script by Wednesday? Oh, by the way, *we* call him, on this side, Santa Claus."

I was left, sucking my pen. I hate trying to write in a hotel bedroom. In the end, I went out and walked blindly along Fifth Avenue, in the twilight, until I came suddenly to the greater blaze of light that was the Rockefeller Centre. Here the crowd of Christmas shoppers were in a solid throng, streaming across the pavements, their heads lifted instinctively towards something so beautiful that it made you feel like a child again yourself. A huge Christmas tree, out there in the square, beside the skating rink, glinting and glowing with silver and frost and a million stars. It was as though one had never seen a Christmas tree before. It meant even more than that. It meant that the whole meaning of Christmas suddenly enveloped you in a cloud of happiness, blotting out loneliness, making you one with everyone else in the crowd of silent pilgrims.

Now the barriers of a stranger in a new country were down.

I hurried back to my hotel, and started to write, talking aloud to myself, like a crazy guy, as I always do when I am working on a broadcast script. But no longer was I afraid of the sound of my own voice, coming back at me from the anonymous bedroom walls. Now I no longer wanted the telephone to ring.

This is what I wrote:

"One afternoon when I stood in the crowd round the giant Christmas tree outside the Rockefeller Centre, I found myself thinking about the message of Christmas, and how Christmas belongs not only to the children, but to all of us, who hold our hands to life, and are grateful to give, because of the overwhelming bounty we receive. . . .

"Nuts! . . . that's what lots of folk would say to that, I know. Fairy tales, rubbish . . . like letting a kid believe in Santa Claus. . . . Well, why not? Surely we should allow our children, encourage our children, to believe in Santa Claus *and* every other fairy story that tends to make life seem a bit more colourful, a degree more romantic, than it does these days to most of us grown-ups, who are inevitably dominated by the reality of atom bombs in cold storage, and world shortages of basic foods . . . and battlegrounds everywhere?

"Youngsters will have to get wise to all that soon enough, won't they? Then why not let them enjoy the sense of peace and security . . . the feeling of everyone living happily ever after, like a fairy story . . . as long as they *reasonably* can? You notice that I emphasize the word 'reasonably.' I would not like you to misunderstand me. I am not for encouraging a state of arrested developments in any child: but I am not for turning them into debunking little pan-faced savages, either. In my view, debunking the fairy-story beauty out of life isn't a profitable pastime for anyone. In fact, all it achieves is to make children afraid of life: all it does is to pour salt into the wounds beneath the healing scars of the last seven years.

"Some of those years I spent at sea, as an ordinary seaman. And one of the memories that will stay with me all my life was the way that at Christmas, my mates would fall to, decorating the ship. We were in the so-called danger zone, but we rigged up a Christmas tree of painted wood and decked it with coloured lights, and one of the stokers, with a vocabulary that would have won medals in hell, dressed up as Father Christmas, using cotton waste for his beard.

"Father Christmas . . . Santa Claus . . . call him what you like. The truth was, that benevolent old gentleman, who instead of sitting in his sleigh, drawn by reindeer, was now enthroned at the end of our messdecks, on a barrel of rum, represented something pretty important and precious to us, though none of us put it into words at the time. It was more than the tots of rum he was ladling out to a long line of happy matelots. I think, looking back, he represented the spirit of fantasy . . . those hidden springs of make-believe, which, encouraged in childhood, can pay such rich dividends in later life, making every sort of crisis bearable, and better still, surmountable.

"In other words, teach children to believe in fairy stories, and they'll never be disappointed by life itself. Why, doesn't everyone know someone in their town or village who was Cinderella in real life, and then, one day, she blossomed into the princess at the ball? Of course we do! Cinderella is one of the most real stories in the whole world, and it's happening all over the world again, every minute, somewhere. I only wish I'd been the author who invented the original legend.

"I first had that thought some months ago, when I was on holiday in Denmark; and one morning in Copenhagen, I set out to pay a pilgrimage and visit a statue which stands in a park, at the end of a long avenue of trees, quite alone. It is the statue of a man with the face of a poet, who sits there serenely, with one hand raised, as though to bless . . . and the other hand holding a book. The inscription at the base of the statue says simply: 'In memory of the fairy-story poet. . . .' While on the other side of the plaque is the picture of a child, riding on the back of a stork in full flight . . . on the wings of imagination.

"Hans Andersen—yes, that was the name, of course—possessed that imagination in abundance. His stories, like the story of the Ugly Duckling, and the Mermaid who walked on swords, and the Snow Princess, will be read by generations of children—and grown-ups, too—long after all the other statues are forgotten . . . and the names of the generals and the politicians, and the trouble-makers, too. Quite forgotten. . . .

"And if you want proof of that, well, there is only one book translated into more languages today than Hans Andersen . . . and that is the Bible. Of course, I know there are those who would like to believe that *that* was the biggest fairy tale of all. But you would not suggest that twice to any of the crew of my ship, who sailed through Arctic waters and beheld the wonders of the deep. While as for the real fairy stories, passed on down the years, like the exquisite Nordic fable of Santa Claus, I would suggest that in a world as dominated by fear and lacking in romance as ours, they play a part today that is more important than ever. For they represent colour, music, beauty, goodness. And what's wrong with that?"

Then I typed out my script, tapping away with two fingers as I always do, even after twenty years of trying to be a writer, and took the envelope myself to the studio. This time, I made my way down Park Avenue, not to stare at the rich apartment houses, where the millionaires live, but to see the long line of Christmas trees, placed a hundred yards apart, right down to Grand Central Station, like one tree reflected in dozens of mirrors, and each reflection more ravishing than the last. I guess, if you asked anyone in New York at Christmas what was the most striking sight in their city, they would tell you that, though some might add, as one mother did to me: "It was not when the lights went full on in Broadway again, but when the Christmas trees were lit in Park Avenue, that I really believed the war was over."

. . . . .

When I had delivered my script, there was nothing left for me to do except idly to find my way back to my hotel, fighting my way among the last-minute shoppers. But I no longer felt alone or frightened by the threat of the solitude of my hotel bedroom. Perhaps it was because of the bridge: the bridge between this broadcast, not yet spoken over the air, and the last one that I had done for the B.B.C. at home, the day before I had left for America. And suddenly now the final paragraphs of that farewell message came back to me, accompanying my step, like a friendly companion. I found I could remember almost every word. . . .

"On Christmas Eve I shall lie awake thinking of my own home, and my own country, and of the most beautiful Christmas tree I have ever seen—(*was it still the most beautiful? Yes, indeed yes*)—in the Church of St. Martin-in-the-Fields. Every year it stands there, at the end of the nave, lit up, with the Star of Bethlehem touching its topmost branch, loaded down with presents, given by everyone . . . perhaps by you . . . for the children who have no parents, no address to which Father Christmas can come. . . .

"I defy anyone to walk down that aisle on Christmas Eve, towards that great glow of coloured lights, and not understand what the message of Christmas really is, how Christmas belongs not only to the children, but to all of us who hold our hands to life, and are grateful to give, because of the overwhelming bounty we receive."

Why were the last words so particularly familiar in my ears? And then I realized it was because I had used them again for this second broadcast, and I had used them again deliberately, because they were the very foundation-stone of my own personal philosophy. For that reason, too, I make no apology for repeating them a second time here, in this short space. I did so equally deliberately, hoping that you may be persuaded to read them yet a third time yourself before turning over the page. . . .

Contrasts

by HELEN HARDINGE OF PENSHURST

YEARS ago, when one entered the big house at Sandringham, the first object that came into the view of the startled guest was an enormous brown bear. Its appearance was huge and ferocious, and it looked alive. Recoiling slightly, it was possible to realize that this was an inanimate object, a trophy of the chase, in fact, a stuffed bear.

On recovering stability, and gaining access to other rooms, it was clear that the house was cluttered up with objects of all kinds, for Queen Alexandra's taste was sentimental; and everything given her by people she loved had a place, from the most beautiful and rare, to the simplest, or even the tawdry—all were affectionately situated, so that she could see them. It would be impossible to imagine dusting such a house, with those contents, now.

She was an old lady at this Christmas time, and still of great beauty and charm—all the more striking as she was extremely deaf, and wore a remarkable auburn wig, about which she never made any pretence. She would simply say, in her deep Danish voice: "My dear child, is my wig on straight?"—without embarrassment to herself or the person to whom she spoke. She was surrounded by old, old people, who had been her lifelong friends: Sir Dighton Probyn, who was himself adorned with a long white beard that was a marvel to us; and Charlotte Knollys, very much muffled up in strange clothes and decorated with amethysts. She survived the Queen, as did also dear Sir Henry

Streatfield, whose kindness and love always made the party warm and friendly.

I speak of Queen Alexandra at Christmas, because her chief characteristic—apart from that charm which neither age nor deafness could affect—was her generosity. She would take you round the house, pressing gifts upon you. She circumvented her staff whenever possible in the distribution of gifts, by sending them secretly; many private letters with five-pound notes were thus sent to people whom she felt might be in need. She was an absolute target for robbers who knew all this, and the people who lived in her household, and looked after her, had the greatest difficulty in protecting her from every sort of imposition. No tramp would come to the door, no old woman looking rather pathetic, no gypsy and child, but if by chance they were seen by the Queen they would get a present; and she always felt that her staff were wrong to try and prevent her, so she just eluded them, and secretly sent out her alms!

She was extraordinarily unpunctual and sometimes nobody got anything to eat in the house, because the bells did not go for meals until the Queen was ready, when they would ring through the corridors—and of course, at that moment nobody else was there! The others would be out, or resting, or occupied, and it used to be a great scramble; but the affection she inspired overcame the constant annoyance caused by these inconveniences.

I associate my first Sandringham Christmas almost entirely with Queen Alexandra, because generosity and Christmastide are such good companions. She was a small woman, but her warm heart would make her reach up to embrace the tallest and most manly of her godchildren: she would throw her arms round his neck and say affectionately: "Ah! My godchild, my godchild!" Her remarkably attractive, deep voice made all that she said sound exceptionally delightful and interesting.

She concealed her deafness with extraordinary skill, chiefly by showing people things, by pointing out the ornaments on her Christmas tree, the arrangement of her presents, ready to give away, and the things that had come from the workshops where ex-Servicemen were employed; and not, of course, listening to one's replies although no one knew this. When she went to church, after the service she would send a message to the visiting preacher on his sermon, saying how good it was, and could she have a copy; she had not heard what he said, but the visiting preacher was always enchanted—as indeed we all were—by her beautiful manners.

Animals, as well as humans, enjoyed her kindness at Christmas-time. She would feed the wild birds in front of the house; a great many cock-pheasants came, as the place was in shooting country, and she seemed to know these cock-pheasants by name, as a Master of Hounds knows his hounds. There would be trouble if any of these birds were missing; this was very difficult, as of course they sometimes got shot—they sometimes even got shot by King George V—and she was always inclined to find fault with this. He was a most devoted son, but it was impossible to recognize a pheasant on the wing as one of those fed by his mother, so these misunderstandings did arise.

The Sandringham Christmas of that day was a family and village affair; although I seem to remember buses being run by outsiders to fill the little church with sightseers.

It was from Sandringham at Christmas that King George V made his first broadcast, and this was to be a yearly feature of Christmas Day in the life of the ordinary English people at home, and overseas. Under many different skies and surroundings have I listened to that voice, and in different companies too. Once, in the tropical night, where, even though it was late in the evening, the windows stood wide open to the moonlight and the sea; inside were candles, on a gleaming polished table, on which stood great bowls of coloured fruits: round the table, a mixed collection of English folk. There, where at every dinner-time the King's health is drunk—as it is wherever an English governor or consul may be—there was a deeper feeling that this voice, at Christmas, was the unseen symbol of that family of nations, to which we all belonged. In this warm night, sitting in that house on a cliff, high above the ocean, the voice which reached out to us from the prosaic English hour of 3 p.m., into our eastern starlight, had a peculiar sense of nearness. Great immensity of sky—star-shine—and sea with its moonlight path: how wide and far-flung you are!—and yet, how near and dear —this familiar voice within the room.

During those rattling, kaleidoscopic years, in various houses through England, the moment of the King's broadcast was kept as a time when even the children listened quietly with the whole household; and it made a communion within the house. People would stand for "God Save the King" at the end of the broadcast: quite big, smart parties would stand round the room, or in groups, sometimes comic in their appearance, but redeemed by the natural simplicity of a common loyalty.

Not much would be said afterwards, but we would go out into the good, fresh air, or the soft moist rain, or tempestuous gales of England, to think all these things over—but to talk of something else.

After the war came, there were many changes in all our lives, and especially many changes at Christmas; the time for rejoicing was taken away. But during those most strenuous years there were one or two moments when it was possible to revive a little the happiness that should belong to the festival. Some children had been forced to remain in London, in spite of the exodus of all their companions. St. Martin-in-the-Fields, that most all-embracing of churches, had gathered in these poor small wanderers, looked after them, taught them, and done what it could to see that they were safe in the streets of London; and one year at Christmas-time with the help of those who minister at St. Martin's, I had a tree at St. James's Palace, a really lovely tree, in spite of the war, and a source of great enjoyment to myself as well as to them. The lights were lit once more for a short time round this symbol of Christ's nativity; and, as we were able to bring to the children a little of what was good in the old unaltered ways, so they brought joy to us. We played games afterwards, slipping about on the rather bare, shiny floors, from which so much of the furniture had gone. And then when it was all over, there was a great deal of washing-up to do; but somehow, the brightness of that evening never faded or got dimmed, even by fatigue at the sink.

Then, during the war, a Christmas pantomime was inaugurated at Windsor Castle, to raise funds for the Merchant Navy, and everyone helped in this—not only by subscribing, but also by taking an active part, where needed, to assist the producer and performers; to paint scenery, or to play in the band, or to help with the costumes. The principal actors were the Princesses, friends of theirs from the locality, and the village schoolchildren, many of whom had come down from London and joined the local school for the war. They were all treated as performers and actors, not as people of any particular class—and indeed, they were of all classes: there is nothing like a good dramatic performance, where your achievement is all that counts, to extinguish any class-consciousness. Of all these occasions, the one I loved most was the Nativity Play, which was put on in St. George's Hall, that great long gallery, with its huge windows lighting up the Garter Shields which ornament the room. There was a raised dais at the end of the room where the play took place. It was beautifully produced: the singing was exquisite, and the ancient drama itself vivid and fresh. This took place at a very bad time during the war, and was a deeply moving presentation. The most striking moment was when the "Three Kings" came in procession, walking up the length of the hall, with Princess Elizabeth, now Queen, leading them. She was dressed in the pageantry of ancient kingship, and carried a casket of figured gold, which had been lent her by her Mother; she moved with beauty and nobility, to offer this to the Infant

Christ. A deep emotion was felt by the audience; and at the end, everyone was snivelling away and swallowing lumps in the throat, and generally presenting an unsightly and shamefaced appearance as they furtively dabbed at their faces. Somebody said: "There's hardly a dry eye in this hall," and the Queen said: "I know, it is such a wonderful old story." But the feeling was more complicated than that: a deeper sense of the present, and of how much we had to lose if the dark hour of the outer world engulfed us—a sense of the beauty of all we cherished most. It was crystallized in this presentation by English children of our worship to the Christ-child; and the essential need in humanity, to cherish what is noble and lovely, and to lavish affection and homage on someone worthy of that devotion.

And last of Christmastide—a dark, cold dawn: it was St. Stephen's Day. I had been ill and in pain. Unable to attend any services during the Christmas season, I went to St. George's Chapel on this day, when there was to be a dedication of a tiny and beautiful early-English chantry as a chapel to St. Stephen. The service took place in one of the narrow side-chancels, where there were very hard, improvised wooden seats for sitting, and an even harder stone floor for kneeling. The soft, pale light of the candles gleamed through the dawn: it was quiet and still; there were very few people; it was quite colourless. We knelt on the cold stone—and my leg began to hurt again. Then, out of the chantry, where a little altar had been erected, but where there was not room for more than two people, stooping under the low pointed arches and stepping down the two steps to come to us, appeared the Bishop in his mitre and robes; and he might have been St. Nicholas himself—so vivid, jewelled, and brightly coloured was his figure in that light—the St. Nicholas of my childhood, always appearing unexpectedly to children. He brought colour, light, glory and a remembrance of picture-books. I think he must have been St. Nicholas.

The colourless shrine of grey stone became the casket of the holy word: the light of day began to glow through the stained-glass, ruby-and-sapphire panes of the windows. The story of St. Stephen's martyrdom was told, and his sense of the heavenly vision pervaded the Chapel, re-creating once more sacred strength within the human heart.

And so disappears St. Nicholas—back to the chantry, amongst the saints—while we rise and go forward with our neighbours, to the good cheer of a Christian and well-earned breakfast.

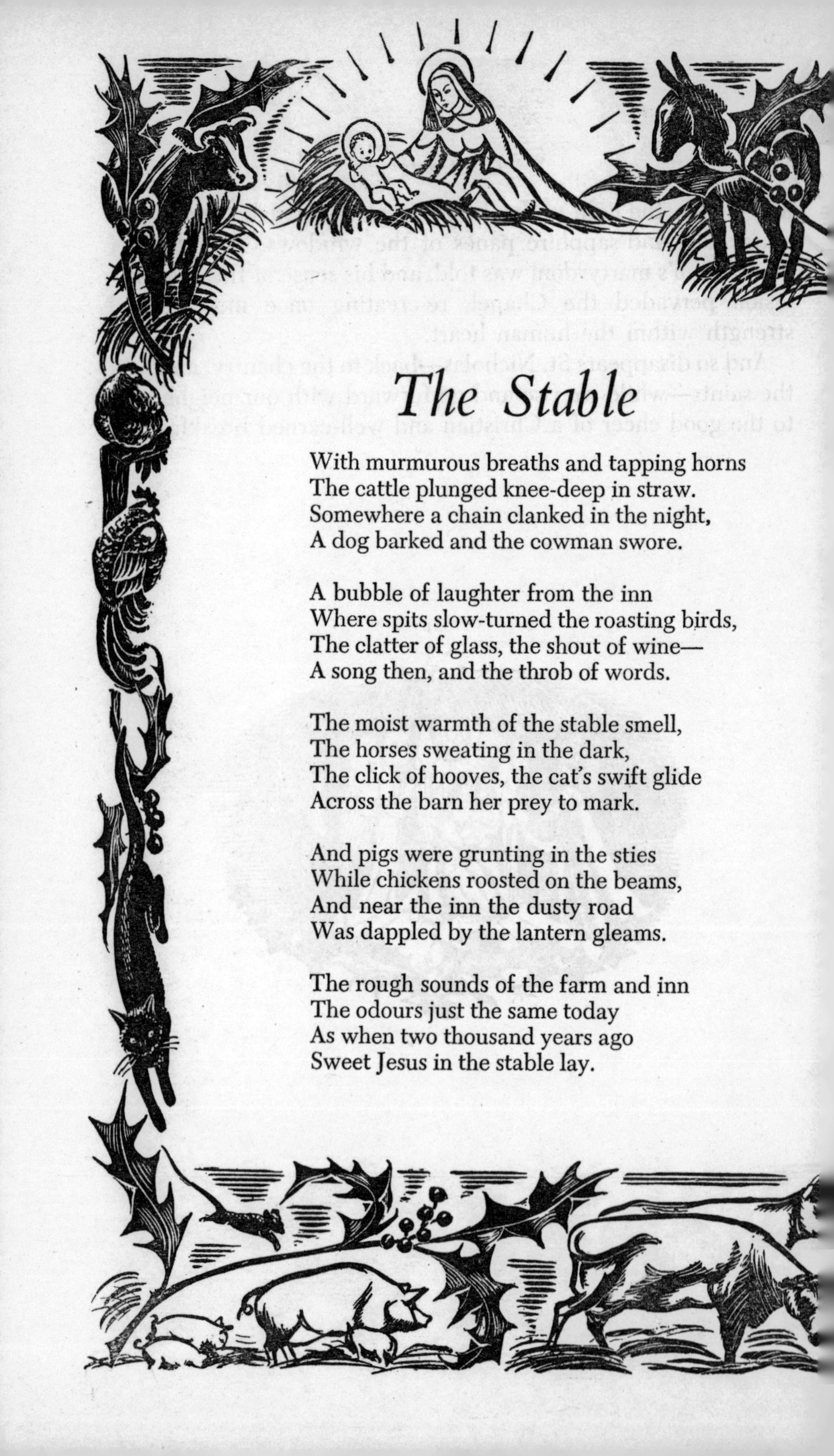

The Stable

With murmurous breaths and tapping horns
The cattle plunged knee-deep in straw.
Somewhere a chain clanked in the night,
A dog barked and the cowman swore.

A bubble of laughter from the inn
Where spits slow-turned the roasting birds,
The clatter of glass, the shout of wine—
A song then, and the throb of words.

The moist warmth of the stable smell,
The horses sweating in the dark,
The click of hooves, the cat's swift glide
Across the barn her prey to mark.

And pigs were grunting in the sties
While chickens roosted on the beams,
And near the inn the dusty road
Was dappled by the lantern gleams.

The rough sounds of the farm and inn
The odours just the same today
As when two thousand years ago
Sweet Jesus in the stable lay.

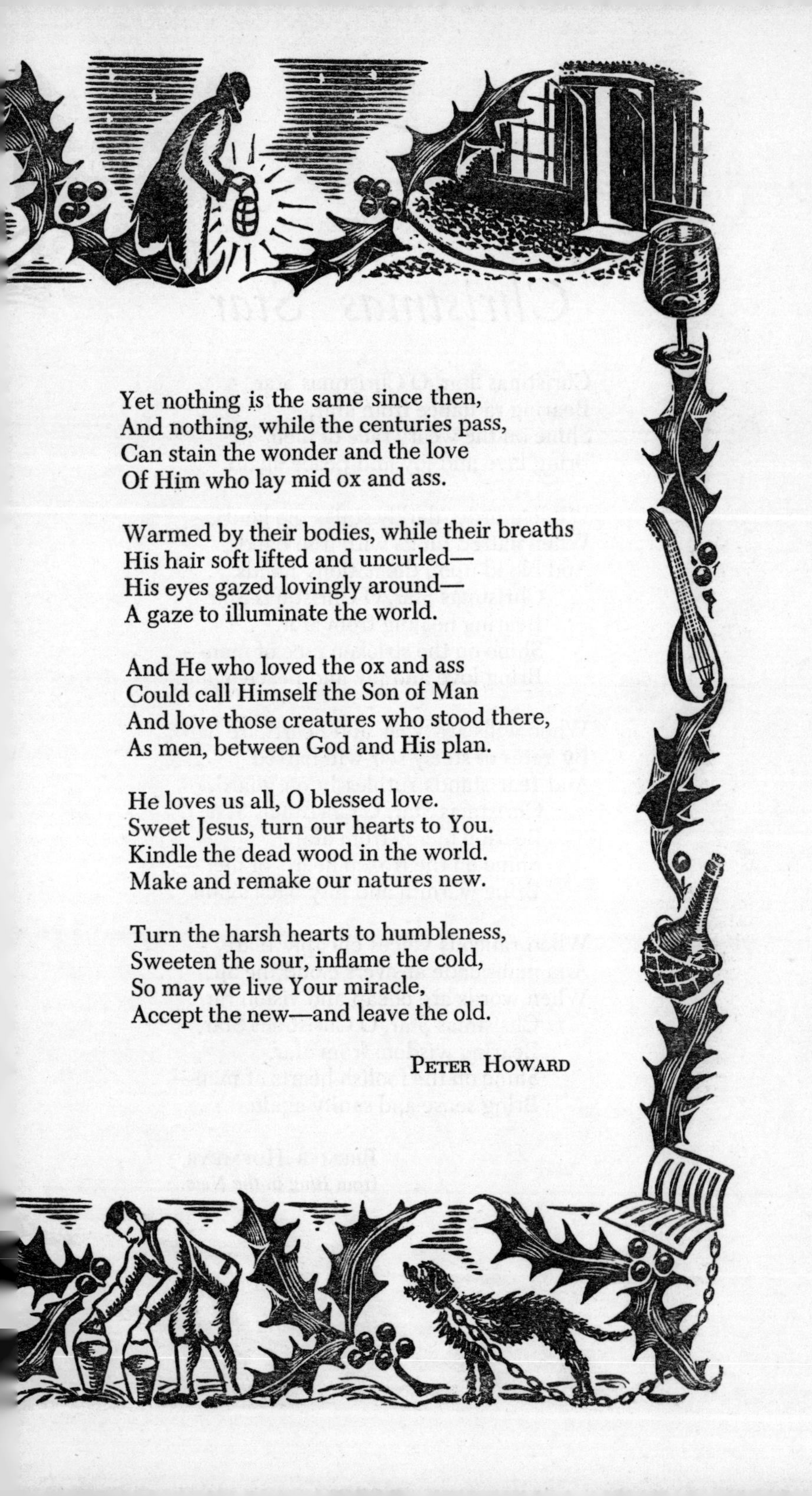

Yet nothing is the same since then,
And nothing, while the centuries pass,
Can stain the wonder and the love
Of Him who lay mid ox and ass.

Warmed by their bodies, while their breaths
His hair soft lifted and uncurled—
His eyes gazed lovingly around—
A gaze to illuminate the world.

And He who loved the ox and ass
Could call Himself the Son of Man
And love those creatures who stood there,
As men, between God and His plan.

He loves us all, O blessed love.
Sweet Jesus, turn our hearts to You.
Kindle the dead wood in the world.
Make and remake our natures new.

Turn the harsh hearts to humbleness,
Sweeten the sour, inflame the cold,
So may we live Your miracle,
Accept the new—and leave the old.

PETER HOWARD

Christmas Star

Christmas Star, O Christmas Star,
Bearing radiance from afar,
Shine on the weary race of men,
Bring love and joy and peace again.

While murder darkly stalks the lands,
When hatred binds with iron bands,
And blood upon the nations' hands,
Christmas Star, O Christmas Star,
Bearing healing from afar,
Shine on the stricken race of men—
Bring love and joy and peace again.

When wills are weak and hearts are hard,
By gates of steely self-will barred
And fear stands ruthlessly on guard,
Christmas Star, O Christmas Star,
Bearing mercy from afar,
Shine on the frozen hearts of men—
Bring warmth and pity back again.

When raucous voices cheaply blare,
And man-made answers cloud the air,
When words are cheap and vision rare,
Christmas Star, O Christmas Star,
Bearing wisdom from afar,
Shine on the foolish hearts of men—
Bring sense and sanity again.

BREMER HOFMEYR,
from *Ring in the New.*

THE FIRST CHRISTMAS

Illustrated by Bridget Peterson

BLANDFORD PRESS LTD. LONDON, W.C.1

SAINT LUKE
Chapter Two
Verses 1-20

AND IT CAME TO PASS in those days that there went out a decree from Caesar Augustus that all the world should be taxed. (And this taxing was first made when Cyrenius was Governor of Syria.) And all went to be taxed, every one into his own city.

AND Joseph also went up from Galilee, out of the city of Nazareth, into Judea, unto the city of David which is called Bethlehem; (because he was of the house and lineage of David;) To be taxed with Mary his espoused wife being great with child.

AND so it was that while they were there the days were accomplished that she should be delivered. And she brought forth her firstborn son and wrapped him in swaddling clothes, and laid him in a manger; because there was no room for them in the inn.

AND there were in the same country shepherds abiding in the field, keeping watch over their flock by night. And lo, the angel of the Lord came upon them, and the glory of the Lord shone round about them, & they were sore afraid.

AND the angel said unto them Fear not: for behold I bring you good tidings of great joy which shall be to all people.

For unto you is born this day in the city of David a Saviour which is Christ the Lord. And this shall be a sign unto you; Ye shall find the babe wrapped in swaddling clothes, lying in a manger.

AND suddenly there was with the angel a multitude of the heavenly host praising God & saying Glory to God in the highest, and on earth peace, good will toward men. And it came to pass, as the angels were gone away from them into heaven, the shepherds said one to another, Let us now go even unto Bethlehem and see this thing which has come to pass, which the Lord hath made known to us.

AND they came with haste & found Mary and Joseph and the babe lying in a manger. And when they had seen it they made known abroad the saying which was told them concerning the child. And all they that heard it wondered at those things which were told them by the shepherds.

BUT Mary kept all these things and pondered them in her heart. And the shepherds returned, glorifying & praising God for all the things that they had heard and seen, as it was told unto them.

How It All Began

by H. WALLACE BIRD

IT HAPPENED in Palestine.

It happened too, in what the Bible calls "the fullness of time." Without knowing it, the world had been prepared for the greatest event of its history.

Sixty-three years before it happened Pompey the Great, invincible Roman conqueror, had entered Damascus. With his legionaries he had marched down the valley of the Jordan to the ford where Joshua, fourteen centuries before, had crossed into the Promised Land. From the Mount of Olives the invader got his first glimpse of the Holy City.

A new chapter in an already long story thus opened in the little country which was the bridge between East and West. To the south was Egypt and the great metropolis of Alexandria; to the north was Antioch, capital of the Seleucids. For Palestine had lain in the path of Alexander's march to India, and later became a buffer state between the two rival kingdoms into which his empire had fallen after his death.

When Rome was completing her conquests and consolidating her frontiers, the coast line of Judæa closed the circle of the Mediterranean. From Palestine, too, the great roads of the Empire ran out across the world. The discovery of new seas and continents has not altered the fact that Palestine is the heart of the earth.

Rome had a variety of ways of administering her conquests. To dominate the world was her passion, and she was not slow to use any handy instrument to that end. In Palestine she found what we have learnt to call a Quisling—Antipater, the Idumæan, who had been minister to the Maccabees, and whose more famous son was to be known as Herod the Great.

Herod's policy was directed solely to safeguarding the crown he inherited from his father. He fawned upon Augustus, after skilfully extricating himself from his earlier flirtation with Anthony. He attempted to purchase the goodwill of the Jews by a judicious patronage of their religion. He rebuilt the Temple and enriched it with new splendours. At the same time he built for Roman and Greek entertainments a theatre within the Jerusalem walls, and an amphitheatre on the plain outside.

Jerusalem, although far from being either well known or important among the cities of the Empire, was nevertheless a watershed of three great streams of culture and civilization which flowed out to the ends of the known world—Roman, Greek and Hebrew. Herod's coins, issued under the tutelage of Rome, bore Greek inscriptions. Roman and Greek words formed a regular part of the current Hebrew vocabulary. So that all might read and understand, the title on the Cross of Christ was written "in letters of Hebrew and Greek and Latin."

If the Romans created the political setting for the arrival of Christ, the Greeks provided the cultural background. The spread of Greek civilization—its language, philosophy, political theory, poetry, art and scientific enquiry—was due mainly to the conquests of Alexander the Great. To this day you can pick up Greek coins in the dust of Taxila in India, and note the Greek features of many of the faces. When Christ came, the educated world had one language, and it was Greek. Most beautiful and delicate of all languages, it was destined to be the vehicle of the Gospel.

But philosophy, literature and art were not enough. With the Greeks, as with the rest, human wisdom had failed. Intellectual subtleties were no defence against moral decline. Cleverness was no substitute for character. Greek depravity hastened Roman corruption. The licentiousness of Greek delicacy put a sordid trimming to Roman bestiality.

The Jews alone had the beginning of the right idea. Like the Greeks, they had spread all across the world the Romans had conquered. Everywhere, even in Rome itself, they were to be found. And wherever they had gone, they carried their religious observances and their Mosaic morality. They made many converts. Their God was the one God, and they alone were God's people. For the Jew recognized only two divisions of mankind—himself and the Gentiles, the Pagans. The Greek looked back to his Golden Age. The Roman was now enjoying his, but the Jew waited. He expected a Messiah. He waits and expects still.

So while they waited they observed the Law, both as it was written in their Scriptures, and as tradition interpreted and demanded. By the time Jesus came, man-made injunctions were more punctiliously observed than the living word of God was honoured. Thus in keeping the Sabbath, almsgiving, fasting and public prayer, they maintained a rigid correctness. It would never have occurred to them to do what was not done.

The synagogue was the local church, and very much the centre of Jewish life. For there, not only was the Law taught and the Scriptures read, but civic and social functions were also held.

Yet, despite the universal observance of religious rite and legal precept, the Jews were not united—except perhaps in their hatred of Rome, and later in their determination to persuade Rome to destroy Jesus.

The Pharisees, themselves of two distinct denominations, were enthusiasts for the Law. They were religio-nationalists, strong in their antipathy to all foreign influence, Greek or Roman. Their piety, exact, severe and legalistic, often turned good men into hypocrites.

The Sadducees were aristocrats, with more concern for politics than religion. With greater respect for Greek culture than the Pharisees approved, they had no faith in the supernatural. For them there were neither angels, spirits nor resurrection.

The Scribes, with the Lawyers, copied the Scriptures and taught the Law.

The Herodians were the government party, but even with these the Pharisees were not slow in making common cause in their machinations against Jesus.

The Zealots were the terrorists. From the time when Pompey first destroyed Jerusalem in 63 B.C. until Titus fired the Temple in A.D. 70 they instigated and led open insurrection and underground resistance. Embittered and fanatical, they not only believed in a Messiah to come, but made it difficult for anyone else to govern meanwhile.

This then was the Palestine in which it happened. At the heart of a world in the grip of military power, enchained in slavery, foul with vice, pierced through with cruelties, the little country, itself torn, bewildered, divided and conquered, kept its pulse beating with the hope of a Deliverer.

. . . . .

So Herod the Great, satrap of Augustus the Emperor, reigned in Judæa.

Among the priests serving their week's turn of duty in the Temple was one named Zacharias. His wife's name was Elisabeth. They were both well advanced in years. They had grown old in grace and faithfulness. They had no children. Once in a lifetime perhaps there came to a priest by lot the much coveted office of burning incense on the golden altar in the Holy Place at the morning and evening sacrifice.

This was Zacharias' red-letter day. He had disappeared within. The great crowd of worshippers waited for him to reappear. Near the golden Candlestick Zacharias saw the figure of a man—it was an angel. He had brought a word from God. Zacharias' prayer was to be answered. Elisabeth was to have a son—a great son. He was to be called John, and he would turn many of his nation to God, making ready for the coming of the Lord those who would answer the call to repentance.

All this was incredible. Zacharias was certainly no exception in being amazed that prayer had been heard. He asked for some proof of what was now told him, a clear and unmistakable sign. A sign was granted, an unwelcome one, and for his doubt he was struck dumb. The people waited, wondering what kept him. When he did appear he could do nothing more than make signs. It was clear that something unusual, even miraculous, had happened.

He finished the days of his week of duty, and returned to his house. Soon the promise was fulfilled. Elisabeth was with child.

Eighty miles away in the Galilæan town of Nazareth Elisabeth had a cousin—young, devout, engaged to be married to Joseph, a carpenter, of the family of King David. Mary was a country maiden. She would know Isaiah's prophecy, "Therefore the Lord himself shall give you a sign; Behold, a virgin shall conceive, and bear a son, and shall call his name Immanuel." She might even dare to hope that she might be the chosen vessel; for secretly in many a maiden's heart was the hope that she might become the mother of the Deliverer.

The same messenger as startled Zacharias in the Temple sought out Mary as she went about her daily round in the home, and made to her the announcement that she had been chosen to be the mother of a Child who was to be called JESUS.

How *could* this be? Mary was unmarried. She made no demand for a sign, as had Zacharias, but asked only for an explanation.

She learnt that the impossible had already happened to her cousin Elisabeth, now within three months of giving birth to her promised son. The same power which had made a mother of Elisabeth in her old age should now make a mother of Mary in her virginity; for with God *nothing* is impossible.

Not for a moment did Mary stop to consider that what for Elisabeth could be nothing other than an occasion of rejoicing and congratulation, for her might be a source of scandal and gossip. All would know. What of her reputation? And even more of her Son's? Whatever thoughts seized her heart as she listened to the angel's news, there was no hesitation in her self-giving. Her surrender to the power of God was unquestioning and absolute. "Behold the handmaid of the Lord; be it unto me according to Thy word." Her body was to be more than temple of the Holy Ghost, it was to be the creative instrument of God's grace and love to the world, and the manner of her self-offering of the very nature of the Son she should bear. His whole life would be submission to the Will of God. She now obeyed as He would always obey. If the first Eve broke man's communion with God through disobedience, Mary, the second Eve, helped to restore it with her whole personality yielded to God's purpose.

Immediately she set out upon the long journey to a village in a lovely valley in the hill country west of Jerusalem to find Elisabeth, to rejoice with her, and to bring her her own astounding tidings.

Where in any literature is there poetry that thrills with life and beauty quite like that which records the meeting of these two women? For here is not only the purest adoration of the heart, but the clarion call of righteous revolution to set the blood a-tingling. These two hearts overflow with the pure joy of the servants of God. Elisabeth is not only to be the mother of the Forerunner, but becomes herself the forerunner of all the millions who down the years would proclaim Mary as "the mother of my Lord." And Mary's heart bursts with praise. Her lips are afire with song, a song sung without ceasing wherever in any language the Church all the world round offers up its worship. Mary's hymn has fulfilled its own prophecy:

> "For He hath regarded the low estate of His
> handmaiden:
> For, behold, from henceforth all generations
> shall call me blessed."

Mary remained with Elisabeth three months, until the eve of the birth of John, and then returned to Nazareth.

Now Joseph was a good man, "and not willing to make her a public example, was minded to put her away privily." To his anxious heart, as in troubled sleep he dreamed, the answer came: "Joseph, thou son of David, fear not to take unto thee Mary thy wife; for that which is conceived in her is of the Holy Ghost."

What came in the dream would corroborate what Joseph had undoubtedly heard already from Mary herself. But the story of the Annunciation, trust and honour Mary though he might, could not have been very easy to accept.

The weeks and months sped by. Mary's time drew very near, when suddenly there went out across the Empire an order from Augustus himself "that all the world should be enrolled." Those who refuse to believe that Jesus was born anywhere but in Nazareth dismiss the idea of the census, but reliable discoveries of census documents make their objections difficult to sustain. Among the Oxyrhynchus papyri was found an order of a Prefect of Egypt which said: "Seeing that the time has come for the house-to-house census, it is necessary to compel all those who for any cause whatsoever are residing out of their home to return to their homes that they may carry out the regular order of the census."

Joseph's ancestral home was in Bethlehem. Thither he must go, and Mary must go with him. They must not be parted now. To take her with him would make her effectively and publicly his wife, and her child his child.

So the eighty miles or more to Bethlehem must be faced. It turned out to be the first stage of a far longer journey which would take them into a strange land before they would see again the familiar streets of Nazareth. How did Mary manage those merciless miles? Where did Joseph contrive to find some warm night shelter and comfort for her? Did the faithful ass bear his load more gently, and pick his way more carefully among the stones and ruts of the tracks and bypaths as they sought to shorten the miles? Come what may now, the baby would be born homeless.

And there, in the City of David, He was born—in a cave among the animals, with a manger for His cradle. No home received Him, come though He had, to be born among His own. Not even the inn opened its doors.

Earth gave Him no welcome, but the skies were alive with strange music. Shepherds on the hills found the watches of the night suddenly lightened, and the velvet silence broken by voices which spelt out to their listening hearts clear directions to guide their steps as they set out in faith for the little town below: "Do not be afraid—go to Bethlehem—you will find a baby wrapped in swaddling clothes and lying in a manger—good tidings to all people—a Saviour—Christ the Lord—on earth peace—men of goodwill." These phrases must have been punctuated with their heartbeat. This was too good to be true—and yet, and yet . . .

They hurried; and they were not deceived. It was true, it was true indeed. Here, lying in the manger in the stable-cave, was the hope of all mankind. They were the first to publish the news; for they went out and "made known abroad the saying which was told them concerning this child." The Good Shepherd's arrival was announced by the shepherds.

Overnight a new age had been born. It came not in as the atomic age came in, with a mighty terrifying spectacle to make the nations tremble, but silently, gently, privately, no more than the stirring of the morning breeze. Rome would die, was indeed already dying. Greece would become, even more, a memory. Jewry, scattered among the nations for generations, would become a byword. This night God had invaded the earth, and of His invasion there would be no end. Here was the answer to power and lust and cruelty and aggression and greed and hate—a little child, come by promise, come by the power of the Holy Spirit, in love, gentleness, humility, splendid without splendour, come to *give.* In a world that knew only how to grasp and get and hold against all comers, He would *give*—truth, life, hope, health, sight, forgiveness, self-respect, and Himself, utterly, until the blood ran down, until with the pain of giving, His heart broke as He died a victim Himself of the cruelty, fear and blindness of the world He had come to change. Here was God's own answer to man's rebellious self-will, the beginning of the culmination of God's unending fight for the hearts of men.

On the eighth day He was circumcised and named JESUS, the Greek form of Joshua, "Jehovah is Salvation." It was no uncommon name. There would be many boys of that name in Nazareth.

On the thirty-third day from His naming, Mary and Joseph and the baby went into the Temple for her purification and the child's presentation.

No requirement of the law must be neglected; for He had come to fulfil, and not to destroy. In the crowded Temple court stood the peasant family with the poor man's offering. "And if her means suffice not for a lamb, then she shall take two turtledoves, or two young pigeons; the one for a burnt offering, and the other for a sin offering; and the priest shall make atonement for her, and she shall be clean."

Drawn irresistibly into the Temple that day was the aged Simeon. The Holy Spirit was upon him, and his footsteps were guided. His heart assured him, old though he was, that he would not die until he had actually seen the Christ. Faith and obedience unveiled his eyes; for as soon as the Holy Family came in he knew that the moment for which his years had been lengthened out had come. Now he was ready to hear God's call whenever it came:

> "For mine eyes have seen thy salvation,
> Which thou hast prepared before the face of all people."

Mary and Joseph marvelled. Deeper, clearer revelation followed. "This child," said Simeon to Mary, "is set for the fall and rising again of many in Israel, and for a sign which shall be spoken against; yea, a sword shall pierce through thy own soul also; that the thoughts of many hearts may be revealed."

Simeon's words found immediate fulfilment. From the distant and expectant East, following a star, there came to Jerusalem the Magi, enquiring where they might find the new king. Herod trembled as tyrants always tremble. The Scribes turned up the Scriptures—the king would be found in Bethlehem; and the parchments were rolled up again. But Herod plotted. In secret conference with these strange and disturbing visitors he furnished himself with what particulars they had to offer, and sent them away to Bethlehem. "Go and search diligently," he said, "concerning the young child; and when ye have found him, bring me word that I also may come and worship him."

The star led them on. They found the house, and within, the Child with Mary His mother. They opened their treasures. At the baby's feet they laid the symbols of His imperishable kingdom. Gold, for His untarnished kingship of the hearts of men; frankincense, for the living, fighting faith of which He would be the great High Priest; and myrrh, the bitter herb of pain and self-denial with which He would purchase His Kingship and Priesthood. The road from the stable-cave where He was born in poverty would lead by way of the Cross to the tomb-cave from which He would rise again as He shattered even the bonds of death to reign in triumph.

The gentle voice of guidance comes in many ways, but the manner of its coming is subordinate to its claim to be followed. So these wise men must first follow a star, and now be redirected by a dream. Supposing the wise had known nothing more than their own wisdom? Could the course of history have possibly remained the same? For guidance is God's way of intervening in human life, and we miss life's point and plan if we miss the guidance of God. It is startling truth, but inescapable, that Christ got into this world because a few people were ready to be guided.

So those seers from the East did not return to Herod, who, cheated of the further information he had expected them to bring, resorted immediately to massacre. So while Jesus was yet a baby, the babies of Bethlehem died for Him. They were the first of a multitude of martyrs to suffer the bitter truth of old Simeon's words.

Joseph also dreamed. "And he arose and took the young child and His mother by night, and departed into Egypt."

Herod's plot failed. The massacre missed its mark.

The Son of God became a refugee.

The White Scarf

by WINIFRED GORICK

BILLY washed himself at the kitchen sink. He had taken off his jacket, for the evening's excitement warranted the inclusion of his neck and ears. The relative importance of his excursions after work could be measured by the extent of his ablutions. For some, a perfunctory rinsing of the hands was sufficient, others merited the addition of a clean face, but the shedding of his jacket presaged a major event.

He wished his clean shirt were ready, but his mother was behind with the ironing, and, in any case, she was unlikely to favour a double change in one week. If only Vera would give him the white silk scarf tonight instead of waiting until Christmas morning. He knew she had bought it for his Christmas present, for he had discovered it one evening last week when he had slipped into her bedroom while she was at the cinema. He had rummaged through her drawer hoping to borrow a pair of socks, and, suddenly, the long box, with its gay design of holly leaves and berries, had shown up from under her bundle of clean handkerchiefs. The temptation to look inside it had been too strong to resist, although he had shut the drawer hastily with a sense of guilt as soon as he had seen the gift card "To Billy with love from Vera." It was against the family code of honour to look at a present beforehand, and he had even tried to forget the contents of the box, but the thought of the gleaming, silken folds of the scarf was constantly with him.

As he dried his neck, steering carefully inside the neckband of his shirt with the thin part of the towel hooked over his first finger, he pictured himself going down to the Club wearing the new scarf. Would the senior boys object to a junior aping their fashions? He would leave his overcoat unbuttoned with the scarf hanging down inside, negligently, as though he did not really care about it. If Mum would give him a new hat he could look "smashing." There was a grand one in green velour at the corner shop, price 12s. 11d. He had only recently started thinking about his clothes, modelling his desires on Joe Bindon, the leader of local fashion. Joe always kept his hat on at the Club, tilted at an angle over his left eye, as he lolled against a wall. It would be a pity certainly to leave a new hat in the cloakroom where it might get lifted.

"Hurry up, Billy, at that sink. You're taking all night to wash yourself and I'm wanting to get on with my baking." His mother's voice was urgent. She was busy at the kitchen table shaping a mould of pastry into which she emptied a cupful of sultanas. Normally Billy would have been close at her elbow, hoping to filch an odd raisin or so. A year ago nothing would have lured him out of the house on Christmas Eve when the puddings would be boiling on the range and Madame Flatts, the rich "fatty" cakes of Lancashire, were being slipped into the bottom of the oven.

The kitchen was warm and colourful, the air heavy with the smell of hot cakes and roasting meat. The scent of orange peel and apples from the jar of mincemeat had a knife-like quality cutting into the odours of cooking as a draught will pierce through a close room. Young Fred was sitting at the table stoning raisins and, for a moment, Billy stood hesitant, the memory of all the Christmas Eves of his experience tugging at his heart. He suddenly had a childish desire to hug his mother. He knew it would be a ridiculous moment to choose, she was far too busy to attend to him, but she looked so big and dependable. He could not define his emotions even to himself. It was as though his mother typified safety and protection from all the buffetings of a life where one had to fight to hold one's own. The largeness of her muscular arms, her wide shoulders and swelling bosom encased in her tight, blue-sprigged overall, seemed the very essence of comfort and loveliness. The world on the other side of the back door was cold and keen and slick, peopled with small-boned, shrill-voiced boys and girls, and strident with swing, noise and competition; here, within the kitchen, was warmth and bigness, motherhood and love. Why not stay indoors, why not be a child for one more Christmas?

"Come on, Billy, the carol singers have left the Club." Jack's voice, clear and insistent, came through the window opening on to the pavement. Billy braced himself. "Good-bye, Mum. So long, Fred." The door banged to behind him and he raced down the street with his friend.

The carol singers were grouped at the corner, the Club Leader giving instructions for their various stopping-places. First to Mrs. Smethwick's in the long row of cottages stretching down Paradise Street—she was ill and would miss the Christmas fun at the Club—then on to Tom Brown's. Tom had broken his ankle on the football field last Saturday and would need to be remembered. After Tom's they would go up the hill to the Aspinall's house. Mr. Aspinall was a butcher and would be generous. Last year he gave ten shillings to their fund.

The group of boys and girls, thirty strong, started off, their boots and clogs clattering over the setts. While they were in the narrow streets of industrial cottages they kept together, but, as they trailed up the steep hill to the larger houses, they broke up into two's and three's. Billy and Jack brought up the rear—they were discussing Billy's rabbits. He had six in hutches in the backyard. He had already saved up thirty-five shillings from his profits. If he and Jack could rent a small plot on the allotments at the back of the town, they could build some hen houses and more hutches and go into partnership together. Both the lads had a supply of Lancashire business acumen. Most of the great mills which they were passing had been started by men who had come from simple homes like their own.

The air at the top of the hill was keen, freshened by the sea breeze sweeping over the plain behind Blackpool. A hundred years ago this part of the town had been open moorland and the road they were following, a narrow track tipping the crest of a range of hills. The trees of the Corporation Park fringed the roadside, the black lace of their branches patterned against the silver-grey of the clear sky. The tall mill chimneys were lost in the darkness of the valley. Away to the left, Billy could see the pale green lights of the Accrington Road, stretched as a necklace across the breast of the town. Immediately below them, the yellow pin-points on the Preston highway turned from the spangled company of the lighted streets for the lonely trek across the fields by Salmesbury to the docks at the Ribble estuary. Billy had never been so far from the centre of the town as this; his home and the lighted kitchen and Mother and young Fred were swallowed up in the bigness of the valley. He no longer wanted to talk about his rabbits, but walked behind the others with his arm over Jack's shoulder in an unaccustomed silence. His companions were hushed too, and, as they turned into the Chairman's garden, the peace of the night stole into their consciousness. The grass was soft beneath their feet and, as Billy felt its resilience, he said:

"I do believe I'm standing on a mat."

"No, you're not, Billy," said the Leader. "It's a lawn."

"Are you sure, Miss?" he asked. "It feels just like a carpet."

She laughed. "Well, if it is, it's a jolly big one, look, it stretches right over there to the flowerbed. Anyway, Billy, are you ready, it's your turn for the solo?"

Billy looked at the softly-lighted doorway leading into the house, then he turned to where the great lawn swept across the hillside, forgetting the others standing behind him. His clear voice rang out over the garden—

"Holy night, silent night, all is calm, all is bright."

The lovely curves of the old German air rose and fell in the quietness of the evening:

> "Round yon Virgin and her child,
> Holy Infant so tender and mild,
> Sleep in heavenly peace,
> Sleep in heavenly peace."

Billy sang on, effortlessly. He had practised the words many times in the clubroom, but, out here in the open, they had more meaning. Pictures formed in his mind; there was the film where he had first heard the carol, with the young priest teaching the words to a crowd of youngsters, tough guys like the boys at their own Club. That was a year or two ago now, but he had always wanted to sing it since then. His thoughts slipped on from the film to the queer oil painting in the local art shop, with the strange, foreign-looking Madonna holding a dark-eyed baby on her knee. The stiff blue folds of her cloak hung about her in a formalism of design which he did not understand. He supposed the Virgin Mary must have looked like that, but he wished she hadn't. He remembered his own mother sitting up in bed last year when Peter was born. He had crept into the room in the early morning; the bedclothes were rumpled from the night and the old green eiderdown was round his mother's shoulders. She was wearing a locknit nightdress, and he had been amazed to see the whiteness of her flesh below the weathered tan of her neck, she was so soft and big, her great arms cradling the baby gently against her breast. Billy had leaned by her, nuzzling into her shoulder as he peered over to look at the child. Peter's face was crumpled and puckered, with black hair standing in damp little spikes over the crown of his head. He was so much younger than the baby in the picture, and, as he had looked at him, his mother had freed her arm and slipped it round Billy, drawing him into the warm circle of this new relationship. There was an elusive scent of powder and Dettol, coupled with a slight pungency from the feathers in the old eiderdown. Every nerve in his body felt doubly alive as though his stomach and his throat shared in the active perceptions of his mind. He struggled for an expression of his thoughts, but could find no words.

"Isn't he beautiful, son?" said his mother, and all he answered was: "Sure."

As he sang, the memories flashed through his mind, blending themselves into an incoherent whole. A new adult comprehension of life was struggling for birth within him. The silence of eternity was caught in the town's mist-shrouded valley, the stillness of the night was as man's awe in the presence of the miracle of birth, the symmetrical design of the blue cloak in the picture the artist's acknowledgement of the soul's incapacity to express the fluid, turbulent depths of thought and worship within the confines of brush and oil. As emotion was imprisoned by bone and flesh, so man's understanding of holiness, love and reverence must ever remain unspoken until the spirit is freed from the bonds of the body.

Billy sang, and the moon shone down on the group of young faces. The children within the Chairman's house called out in excited voices: "Mother, Mother, the carol singers are here," and they ran to open the inner door. The smell of hot mincepies followed in their wake, and, as the singers crowded into the hall the glass bells tinkled gaily on the Christmas tree in the corner, so that the house was filled with the scent and noise and bustle of Christmas.

Half of the carol singers squeezed into the dining-room, the others filed into the lounge, their eyes shining with curiosity as they viewed the modern luxury of the room. Billy bounced up and down in the huge upholstered armchair, his thin fingers sensing the velvety pile of the cushions.

"Look, Jack, a pianer with legs. Coo, what a chair! I'm here for the night. What's that?" as he saw the bell-push. "Do you press it and does the whole fireplace come down?" His excitement made him talkative.

The Chairman brought in hot drinks and they talked of their

carol singing and of the Christmas Play at the Club on Boxing Day. Billy leaned back in the armchair, and as he relaxed, his mind leapt on to the thought of the white scarf. What a pity he was not wearing it tonight! He had never been in the lounge of one of these larger houses before. Joe looked grand in his, sitting over there by the vase of chrysanthemums, with his chest thrown out and the scarf hanging down on either side, catching the lamplight in its folds.

There was a sound of voices from the dining-room as the rest of the party prepared to leave. The other boys and girls began to button up their coats. Billy snuggled deeper into his chair, shutting his eyes. "You go on," he said, "I'm staying here for ever."

They crowded to the door and into the hall and, for a brief moment, Billy was alone. He darted across to the piano and brushed his fingers over the keys, the ivory smooth as taut silk against his skin. He could see his thin face reflected in the polished depths of the wood. The length of the room stretched in front of him, the cool white walls a foil for the design of glowing mahogany, cumbrous deep-seated chairs, and the vivid gold of the cushions slashing the shadows beyond the arc of the lamps. The room had a quality of space and beauty akin to the detached loveliness of the moonlight resting on the mist of the valley. Again he was filled with a sense of frustration, his child's mind, as yet too untutored and inexperienced to comprehend the range of his own spiritual vision, was too narrow a vehicle for the flow of fresh impressions. An impish smile flew over his face and he brought his hands down on the keys in a clashing discord.

"Billy, what are you doing?" called out a horrified voice from the group in the hall.

"Come on, young man, you'll be up to some mischief in a moment," said the Chairman's husband in a bantering tone as he came into the room. "You'd better hurry, or you'll be late for your potato-pie supper, it's past ten o'clock."

Billy scurried past him and soon his voice was joining in lustily with popular songs as he linked arms with the lines of boys and girls swinging down the hill to the town.

"Noisy young devils," said the respectable townsfolk as they prepared for their beds. "The youth of today hasn't a thought beyond public houses and rowdy behaviour."

As Billy opened the back door of his home he was greeted with a shout of laughter, Uncle Jack and his father were standing by the kitchen fire and a long-legged, dark-eyed man was seated in the rocking-chair. Young Fred was putting the knives and forks on the table, and Vera and his mother were busy cutting up bread in the back kitchen.

"Oh, here you are, Billy," said his father. "Supper's just about ready, lad. Come in and warm yourself, it's starvation outside."

'Is that you, Billy?' called his mother. 'I'm glad you're no later, bring some chairs in from the parlour, we shan't have enough for everyone in here. Your Aunt Ethel and Uncle George will be along in a moment."

He was swept up into the preparations for the family party. The men were busy discussing football technicalities. Their local team had a national status and Billy listened eagerly to snatches of their talk as he ran about for Vera and his mother.

"Who's the chap in the rocking-chair, Mum?" he asked, as he watched her carve the beetroot into wafery slices.

"You'd better go to our Vera for that information," his mother answered with a laugh. "Do you mean you've forgotten him, Billy? Don't you remember Billy Hodson who used to go to school with our Vera before the war? No, I suppose you were too small—ee, time does go! Well, anyway, lad you ask Vera and she'll tell you. Now take this beetroot in and put it at the end of the table, and mind you don't spill the vinegar on the cloth."

Billy carefully steered his way back into the kitchen. The table was fast being filled. The fatty cakes with the rich fruit bulging through their crisp, flat surfaces, were piled up in the centre. They were flanked by a huge jar of yellow pickles and a dish of mincepies. A plate of boiled ham was at each place and every spare corner was used for some home-made delicacy. Billy's mouth watered. He was hungry after his long evening out of doors and he hoped the grown-ups would not take too long to start. Vera stood at the end of the table, counting the places, everything seemed ready.

"Our Vera looks all right tonight," thought Billy. "That's a swell blue dress she's wearing." And again the new world of his mind went racing ahead, lifting him out of the kitchen to the realm of carols and moonlight and the blue of the Madonna's cloak in the picture. As Vera moved her hands from her hips Billy saw the ring encircling her third finger.

"Who gave you that, Vera? Isn't it a beauty, is it a Christmas present from Dad?" There was a sudden quietness in the room as his question was taken up by a great laugh from his father.

"Well, of all the suggestions! No, my lad, I'm not out to marry my own daughter. You'd better come and see this chap in the chair here, he'll give you a better answer."

His father reached out and put a hand on his shoulder and Billy found himself twisted round and facing the man by the fireside. The dark eyes smiled at him.

"Well, Billy, you don't remember me, you were a right little chap when I was last in England, but we'll be seeing a good deal of each other in the future. How will you like two Williams in the one family? Do you think you can put up with a big brother?"

"Sure," said Billy, shaking the outstretched hand. He was not at all sure, but it seemed the only thing to say.

There was a knocking at the door.

"Here's Ethel and the others," said his father. "That's good, now we can get down to things. Bring the potato pie in, Mother, and let's get started."

Billy slipped down to a seat at the end of the table next to young Fred, the thought of Vera's engagement overshadowed by the gargantuan feast. He watched his mother cutting the crust of the potato pie and sniffed at the delicious smell of hot onions.

"I hope they leave us some," he whispered to Fred as he watched the numerous portions served round the table. His mother knew that he liked his pastry very crisp. He thought the brown piece where she started would go to Aunt Ethel, but no, trust his mother, she worked her way anti-clockwise round the pie, her experienced eye balancing the portions with a mathematical precision. The nicest piece of all arrived on Billy's plate, and he heaved a great sigh as he dug his fork into his helping.

The supper lasted well into the small hours of the morning. In industrial Lancashire no one ever goes to bed on Christmas Eve until it is close on the time when the "knocker-up" a few years ago would have been making his rounds, tapping on the windows to rouse the sleepers for the day's work in the mills. As Billy went upstairs to bed his mother called him into her room. Young Fred was already in his bed in the corner and Peter was asleep in his cot. Spread out on the green eiderdown of his mother's big double bed was a pair of blue and white striped pyjamas. Vera was leaning over the brass rail at the bottom of the bed, her eyes shining with excitement.

"Listen, Billy," said his mother. "You'll have to have your present from Dad and me tonight. I don't like not giving you a surprise in the morning, like we always do, but we've had to put the camp bed down in your room for Vera's Billy, and Vera doesn't want you to sleep there in your old shirt. You're getting big now, and I thought you'd like some proper pyjamas, you've never had a chance to have them before."

Billy looked at the striped garments suspiciously.

"Oh, Mum, I don't want to wear things like that. I'm more comfortable in my shirt."

Vera's voice broke in, high pitched and excited.

"Don't be so silly, Billy. You can't shame me by wearing an old shirt in front of Billy. Mum's bought these specially for you and it's only having your present a little bit early, it's nearly Christmas Day now. Be a good lad and wear them for my sake, look they fit you splendidly." She held the coat against his chest.

"It's grand, Billy, you look a real man."

"All right," said Billy gruffly. It was difficult to refuse Vera when she looked so pretty with her bright colour and soft, wavy hair. "You're not to come into my room though, I don't want anyone to see me in them."

"Of course I won't," said Vera. "But you will wear them, won't you, word of honour?" Billy made no answer; reluctantly he rolled the garments under his arm and turned into his room.

There was hardly space to undress with the camp bed placed at the side of his own small iron bedstead. He pulled off his clothes, throwing his boots with a satisfying bang against the opposite wall. He was swearing softly under his breath, words he would never have dared to say in front of his mother. The whole thing was Vera's fault, bringing that fool fellow into the house. He didn't want a strange chap in his room, and what did it matter if he did sleep in his shirt? All the other lads at the Club did the same, only the stuck-up softies at the Grammar School wore things like this. It was just like a girl to do such a thing. He pulled on the trousers and felt a sharp stab in his back; he twisted them round and gave an exclamation of pain as a pin scratched his waist, leaving a thin, spotted line of blood on the fabric. He looked at the price ticket, 12s. 11d., and, as he did so, the realization came to him that this was his Christmas present from his parents. The new hat he had so cherished in his imagination would not be his. He heard the men moving downstairs, and hastily pushing his way into the pyjamas, he jumped into bed, drawing the blankets up over his head.

His door opened, and he heard whispering voices in the doorway as Vera came to say "good-night." Then there was a creak as the newcomer stood on the loose board between the beds, to undress.

"Are you asleep, Billy?" he whispered. Billy did not answer, and, within a few moments, the light was switched out.

The pyjamas felt hot and stuffy; stealthily Billy untied the waist cord and slipped his legs free. Gritting his teeth, he pushed the trousers into a corner of the bed, gaining a little satisfaction as he felt their stiff newness crumple up beneath the action of his feet. The familiar freedom of his bare legs eased his bad temper. He lifted the blankets away from his face and put his arms behind his head. The pillow was cool and the warmth of the pyjama jacket was pleasant. As his body relaxed, his temper disappeared. Perhaps he could manage without the new hat. The scarf would look nearly as good by itself, and, after all, it was bad manners to wear a hat indoors even at the Club. He could hardly blame his mother for not knowing what he had wanted; he had not explained to her that he had been building up a mental picture of such new finery.

The moon was shining in at the window. Sleepily his thoughts slipped back to the Chairman's garden. It had been a grand Christmas Eve, with the carols and the potato pie and Christmas pudding. Phrases from the carols sang through his mind, and within a few moments he was asleep.

It had long been a practice in their family for the presents to be given out after breakfast. They were packed up carefully by their respective donors and stacked on the kitchen dresser, and then, as soon as the breakfast dishes had been cleared, Dad would seat himself at the head of the table and pass the presents round. The parcels were of all shapes and sizes, but Billy could see the long, narrow, holly-decorated box which held the scarf, sticking out at the base. Everyone was in high spirits, even Peter seated in his high chair seemed to understand that this was no ordinary breakfast-time. Billy waited breathlessly, his share of the parcels mounting up before him, but his thoughts were centred entirely on the white silk scarf. There was a bulky package from Uncle George, an unexpected flat-shaped parcel from Mrs. Denman. He had carried her coals in for her during the winter. At last there only remained the decorative box, and Billy could see the label which had become so familiar to him, "To Billy with love from Vera."

"And now," said his father, as though he were addressing a Union meeting, "I come to the most important gift of all. Mr. William Hodson has not been with us very long, but I understand that our Vera has been spending most of her pocket money on stamps for daily letters, and now, at last, William II is home in England. This parcel appears to be addressed to him. At one time, such a label would have been for our own young Billy, but, if Vera gives her love to anyone now, it surely must be to Mr. Billy Hodson." The family clapped their hands and Peter joined in with his spoon on his plate. There was general laughter and everyone started unpacking the gifts.

Billy found his eyes smarting. He untied the string round his own parcels, a wallet from Aunt Ethel, a set of tools from Uncle George. Vera's was at the bottom, it was small and slim—a propelling pencil. Under the cover of the general "thank-yous" he slipped out to the backyard and shut himself in the lavatory. It was the only place in the small, crowded house where he could be alone. In the half-light he kicked at the whitewashed wall in a fury of temper and disappointment. What a fool he had been. Of course, Vera would never have given him such an expensive present. He ought to have known that something like this would have happened when she had talked about her boy friend coming home. Somehow, he had never taken her letter-writing seriously, all grown-up girls did queer things, like sitting for hours knitting a jumper or making a rug. He had never imagined that she would bring a man home, making him share his bedroom with a stranger and wear beastly pyjamas, even taking his name and now his Christmas present. He had wanted that scarf more than anything else in the world. What would Jack think of him after all his boasting? He knuckled his eyes, tears coming despite his unwillingness.

He heard the muffled sounds of the breakfast dishes being washed up. "Where's Billy?" called Vera. For a moment he pricked up his ears, then he realized she was not asking for him. It seemed like a direct insult.

Well, he couldn't stay out here all the morning. He jolly well wouldn't let Vera know what he had been expecting. He dried his eyes on a grubby handkerchief, rubbing his face with his hands, blissfully unaware of their dirtiness. He had better feed his rabbits. He slipped out into the yard. The cold air made him feel better, it tightened up the skin on his cheeks. The rabbits were hungry, for it was long past their normal breakfast time, and he got their feed from the bin standing in the shed. He poured some of the grain into his hand and held it inside the hutch. Martha, the big grey doe, snuffled into his palm. Well, at least, his rabbit loved him even if his family didn't care whether he lived or died. It would do them good if he just disappeared, perhaps he'd go to America, they wouldn't need him now Vera was going to have a husband.

His mother's voice came from the kitchen. "Billy, you'd better be going down to Mrs. Denman's to thank her for your present. She'll need her coals brought in for the holiday. Don't be too long doing your rabbits."

He did not answer beyond a grunt under his breath. If he went to Mrs. Denman's he would not have to face his family for a while. It was a good idea. He knew his mother would insist that he washed before going out, so he shut the door of the hutch quietly and hurried out of the back gate.

He returned in time for dinner and found the house strangely quiet. Vera and her Billy had disappeared. She was spending the night at his family's house. Peter was asleep and young Fred was visiting Aunt Ethel. His mother was tired and did not seem to notice his moroseness, perhaps because it had not affected his appetite. He ate a large helping of pork and vegetables and asked for more cold Christmas pudding. Luckily there was not much washing-up for such a small party. He knew he would have to help. The best thing seemed to be to try out his new tools. He could shut himself in the back kitchen.

He did not meet the other Club members until the next evening. He knew Jack would be expecting him to wear the new scarf, and as he put on his shabby overcoat his resentment rose within him with fresh force. When one was a kid one didn't care about clothes, but his mother might have done something about his things, now he was out at work. After all, she had his wage every week. Fancy giving a chap a pair of pyjamas when he needed a coat and hat.

The Club was gay with chains and coloured lights and the grey velvet curtains were drawn across the stage at the far end of the large recreation room. Jack met him downstairs.

"You're wanted by the producer as soon as you come in, Billy," he said. "Harry Henshaw's ill and I think you've got to take his part. You'll have to hurry." No word about the scarf, thank goodness for that!

He went upstairs to the Club lounge where the actors in the Christmas Play were being made up.

"I'm so glad you've come, Billy," said the Leader. "Could you be one of the three kings? You can double the part with your solo in the first act. Look, here is your costume. Come in here after the opening choir and get dressed while the rest of the play is going on. Hurry up everybody, we ought to be starting in a few moments. The choir of angels must take their places in the wings now."

Billy was hustled out of the room with the others. The stage was set for the shepherd scene, and, as he peered through the wings, he saw to his surprise that the backcloth depicted the local moors. Longridge Fell was on the skyline, the dry-stone walls dividing it into patterned squares, and the cluster of houses by the river bank bore the outline of Ribchester. The scoutmaster had painted the scenery and he had drawn his inspiration from the Lancashire hills. The stage lighting was toned down, the hall plunged in darkness, and the shepherds took up their places. As Billy sang, he found the hardness in his heart disappearing, the effortless range of his voice swept him as always into a magic world where the very essence of his being seemed to find freedom, and, as he bade the shepherds rise up and seek the Lord, he forgot his shabby suit and the disappointment that had spoiled his Christmastide.

He stood in a dream as the curtain fell, caught in the spell that music wove round him.

"Come along, Billy, you can get into your costume now." The Leader put her hand on his shoulder and they turned into the dressing-room.

"I'll make up your face first," she said. "You'll want to be a good bronze colour. You see, you've been travelling a long way and the sun and the wind have burnt your skin as you have come across deserts and mountain ranges."

He sat in a chair and she made up his face swiftly. He rarely saw the Club Leader alone. It was queer having her looking after him like this. She was older than Vera and younger than his mother, yet she seemed half like a sister. You could talk to her as though she had known you ever since you were little.

She helped him into the long red skirt of his robe. The tunic buttoned high at the neck and was heavily embroidered in gold thread. She flung a rich velvet cloak over his shoulders and placed a three-tiered crown on his head. She looked at him critically and then turned to the costume cupboard. Billy watched her moving the hangers along. Once again his normal everyday self seemed to be disappearing; it was fun to be a king. She came up to him and in her hands she held a length of white silk, bordered with long tassels.

"I think this is just what the costume needs," she said. "It will give you a slightly priest-like air. I always feel that the last King who brought myrrh to Our Lord represented us ordinary Christians. You know that myrrh means sorrow, don't you, Billy? and it is those of us who have so much in life who seem to give Him pain. I've been so horribly ungrateful about some things this Christmas, and I felt so ashamed of myself when it came to planning this play tonight."

"What does myrrh look like, Miss? Do I carry it in my hands?"

"No, Billy, we're not having any actual gifts. You'll come up from the back of the hall, after the other two kings have gone on to the stage, and you'll cup your hands, so, and you'll sing the last verse from 'We Three Kings.' You know the words. But, as you sing, try to imagine all the gifts you are going to take to Him. They'll not be happy, pleasant things like the others, but all the badness in your own heart, all the bitterness and ingratitude in the whole world. They are ugly gifts, but they are some of the presents that we men took to Christ when He lived among us. Because He loves us so much He takes them and changes them into goodness and love and all the things that make life worth while. You know yourself how, if you are feeling cross and beastly and someone is awfully kind to you, the bad temper just disappears like snow in the sunshine. It's a little bit like that. Use your imagination, Billy, and you'll understand.

"Look now, the second act is ending, and you'll have to be ready to go on. Wait until the hall is darkened and slip out at the back. Walk slowly, remember you are a king."

Billy waited a few moments, then he walked over to the mirror. He did not recognize himself. The tall crown gave him height and the dark make-up lent an air of maturity and fullness to his face. It was as though he too had stepped into the realm of colour and mystery that belonged to the Madonna of the picture. The long scarf hung in heavy folds from his shoulders, its whiteness emphasized by the scarlet of his robe. He picked up the weighted tassels, sliding them through his fingers, their touch was curiously satisfying—he *was* wearing a scarf after all tonight.

The hall was in darkness, the close-packed audience but blurred lines of shadow. In the last two chairs of the back row

Vera and Billy Hodson were sitting together, the coveted white silk scarf showing above his coat collar.

Billy looked at the narrow aisle stretching in front of him. As he raised his eyes to the stage, his mind was thrown back to the Christmas Eve when he had stood on the heights overlooking the town. The artist had taken his scene from the same vantage point, but the mist had lifted from the valley and the factory chimneys stood out stark and grim, pin-pricked with light from their myriad windows. In the distance the great hills bordered the skyline.

It seemed as though a shelter had been fashioned from the darkness of the streets and, against a timeless black background Mary sat with her Child. Her blue cloak fell in stiff, rich folds around her, her eyes were dark and shining, and, on her knee a tiny baby, as small as Peter had been a year ago, waved his hands. The shepherds were grouped around the Madonna, but, over behind them, mechanics and carpenters, business men and mill girls, ordinary men and women of today, knelt in adoration.

As Billy moved forward, singing the sad words of the carol, his spirit suddenly found articulation. With a new, swift perception he saw his temper and his covetousness, his jealousy and possessiveness, as the wretched gifts which he had as a small boy, to offer. A chap simply could not take miserable things like that. He paused for a moment as he made his slow way to the stage, and turning deliberately, he smiled at Vera's Billy as he sat beside her in his white scarf.

When he reached the stage the Child stretched out His hands and smiled at him and, bending low with the dignity of a king, Billy took off his long white scarf and laid it with the other gifts at the Child's feet.

Sailor's Christmas

We lay in Iceland winterbound,
And heard the blizzard blow,
And naught we saw on sea or shore
Except the driving snow.

Then said our Captain to the Cook,
At anchor as we lay,
"Make us a duff with all your might;
Tomorrow's Christmas Day!"

Then said the Cook, "A Scotsman I,
My season's Hogmanay,
Yet will I make a mighty duff
To eat on Christmas Day."

On Christmas Day it still snowed on,
No news from home had we,
But we'd the Cook's great Christmas duff,
And our good company.

The wind blew wild, the snow it piled
On decks your boot would freeze on,
But in the mess-deck down below
We kept the Christmas season.

With paper streamers all was rigged,
The officers were messmen,
Of seamen, stokers, bunts, and all,
None greater were nor less men.

And there was light and warmth and cheer,
No plate nor glass stood empty,
A genial glow lit every heart
Of all our eight and twenty.

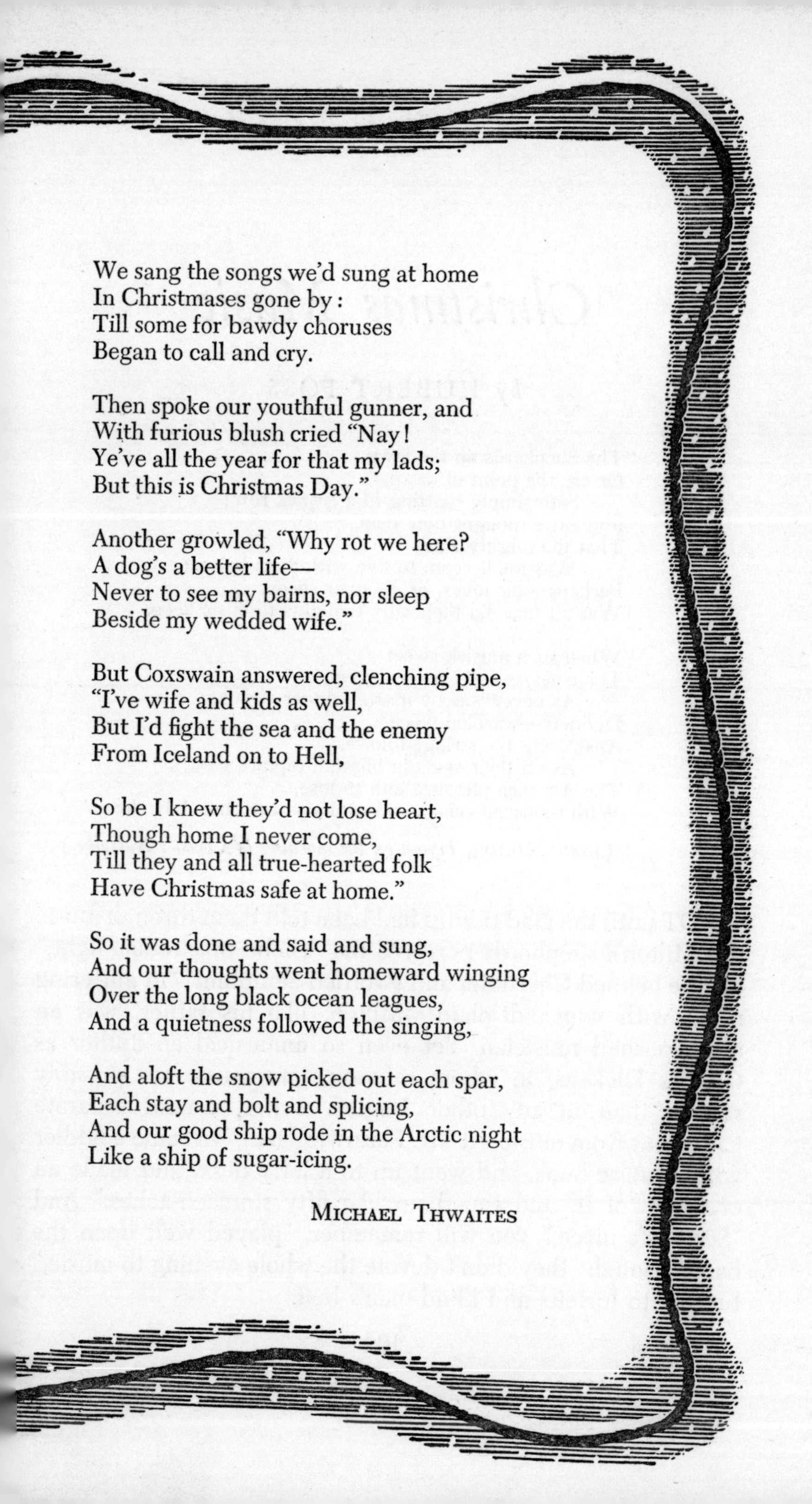

We sang the songs we'd sung at home
In Christmases gone by:
Till some for bawdy choruses
Began to call and cry.

Then spoke our youthful gunner, and
With furious blush cried "Nay!
Ye've all the year for that my lads;
But this is Christmas Day."

Another growled, "Why rot we here?
A dog's a better life—
Never to see my bairns, nor sleep
Beside my wedded wife."

But Coxswain answered, clenching pipe,
"I've wife and kids as well,
But I'd fight the sea and the enemy
From Iceland on to Hell,

So be I knew they'd not lose heart,
Though home I never come,
Till they and all true-hearted folk
Have Christmas safe at home."

So it was done and said and sung,
And our thoughts went homeward winging
Over the long black ocean leagues,
And a quietness followed the singing,

And aloft the snow picked out each spar,
Each stay and bolt and splicing,
And our good ship rode in the Arctic night
Like a ship of sugar-icing.

MICHAEL THWAITES

Christmas Music

by HUBERT FOSS

"The Shepherds on the lawn,
Or ere the point of dawn,
Sate simply chatting in a rustick row;
Full little thought they than,
That the mighty *Pan*
Was kindly com to live with them below;
Perhaps their loves, or els their sheep,
Was all that did their silly thoughts to busie keep.

"When such musick sweet
Their hearts and ears did greet,
As never was by mortall finger strook,
Divinely—warbled voice
Answering the stringed noise,
As all their souls in blissfull rapture took:
The Air such pleasure loth to lose,
With thousand echo's still prolongs each heav'nly close."

(JOHN MILTON, *Hymn on the morning of Christ's Nativity.*)

NOT until the glad tidings had been told them through music did Milton's shepherds perceive the "Globe of circular light," or "the helmed Cherubim and sworded Seraphim" "in glittering ranks with wings displaid." Milton, like his father, was an accomplished musician. Yet even so unmusical an author as Charles Dickens, in whom references to music are possibly scarcer than in any other English writer, cannot separate Christmas from music. At Mr. Fezziwig's ball, "in came a fiddler with a music-book, and went up to a lofty desk, and made an orchestra of it, and tuned up like fifty stomach-aches." And "Scrooge's niece," you will remember, "played well upon the harp," though "they didn't devote the whole evening to music," turning to forfeits and blind-man's buff.

So it has been, music as the natural expression of Christmas, since the dark austerities of the Middle Ages. "On Christmas night all Christians sing," says the carol, "to hear the news the angels bring." But the graph-line of joy and music is not level; it wavers with the changes in taste of each period. There is a high peak in the line, and a low trough, and I for one will not attempt to adjudge the present level. But one cannot help remembering *Marmion,* where Scott writes:

> "England was merry England when,
> Old Christmas brought his sports again . . . .
> A Christmas gambol oft could cheer
> The poor man's heart through half the year."

There is a touch of *pastiche* here, of the memory (in 1808) of a happier English past.

It is a feeling, a nostalgia, that has affected most people as they grow older since the Industrial Revolution made "those dark satanic mills" in "England's green and pleasant land." We find this feeling in many strange places—in our own desire, so often expressed, for "some of the old favourites" in our carol singing—many of them rather paltry pieces of Victorian genre. We have, in uncritical Christmas mood, very little sense of antiquity. We like what we know, but do not necessarily know what we like, and certainly do not know what we might like. Our terms of reference are family memories, which means a Victorian tradition, dating perhaps from great-grandfather, according to our ages today. An old tramp I knew, named Happy (and no more), recommended me some years ago to a singer who would sing me old songs; "some," he said, "from the time of Jesus Christ, and some older than that, from the time of God A'mighty." He was illiterate. His sense of antiquity was, however, better than ours when we are "dreaming of a white Christmas," or gaily singing the purely fictitious story of Good King Wenceslas. Or else, we become exaggeratedly "Christmas conscious" like the Americans, who, when I was last in Chicago, for the week before 1938's Christmas, flooded the main streets with carols from sidewalk loudspeakers, at the most unsuitable hours, until a carol-lover could have screamed. "Wenceslas" makes a poor piece, dating from 1853, and yet it is an "old favourite"—one of the carols we *must* have.

Compare it—read the other words first—with the vigour of this carol:

Ex. I*

That carol tune, which appears to date from somewhere about 1520, is not only traditional, but spontaneous. When Dickens conjured up the ghosts of Christmas Past and Christmas Present, he was (though I am not sure he knew it) following in the trail of the medieval "mystery plays." Here, Sir Christmas comes before us, not in prose, not in the *oratio obliqua* of fiction, but in person, and is greeted by the company, who sing his welcome, and he enjoins them in his splendid free melody to "Make good cheer and be right merry, And sing with us now joyfully": he has told us, most directly, the eternal news of Christmas, the news that is not to be celebrated in reminiscence, not in a

*From the *Oxford Book of Carols*, by courtesy of the Oxford University Press.

picture-postcard fashion of an old ceremony, but in a new and fresh announcement every year.

For Christmas is not an ending period, nor is it a sentimental family occasion. It is a renewal of life that comes, in our way of thought, on a date near to the end of the year. That date was not the chosen moment for celebrating the birth of Christ before the fifth century A.D., and not for joyful expressions until nearly a thousand years later. Yet a pagan festival was held in Britain on December 25th long before its conversion to Christianity. The dates of the Roman Saturnalia came very near to those of our Christmas (up to December 19th), "and provide" (so authority writes) "the prototype, if not the origin of our Christmas festivities." Such was the spontaneity of the makers of our carols (I will not insult them by calling them writers) that we find continual traces of pagan legend and habitude leading us to the story of Christ's birth. I quote a clear example:

Ex. II*

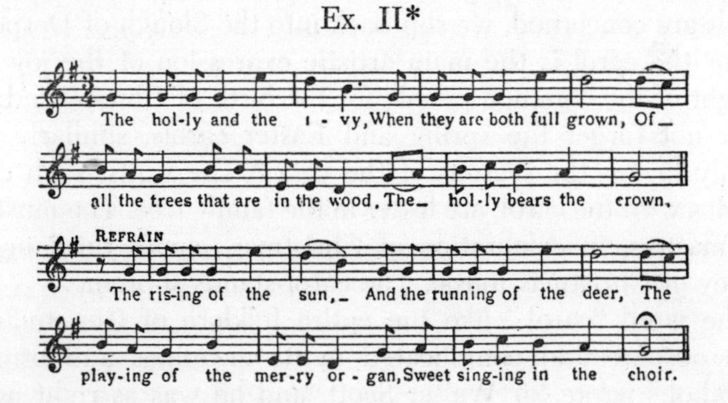

The symbolism is palpably adapted to the new ideals of Christmas in the Renaissance from the nature worship of Druidical days. The holly represents the man, the ivy the woman, and the "merry organ" is brought in as a later counter-symbol. Percy Dearmer quotes Chaucer's "Nun Priestesses Tale" in parallel.

*By courtesy of Novello & Co. Ltd.

Out of the grim and murky blackness of the Dark Ages, that undefined period of ascetic fight by Christianity against surviving barbarism, a light begins to shimmer with St. Augustine, flickers for a time, and at the end of the first millennium is burning secretly but steadily. Christmas music was established early as an inseparable part of the new enlightened attitude towards the Christian belief. The "mysteries" and "miracles" and *Sacre Rappresentazioni*—those firmer founders of opera than even Peri and Cavalli and Monteverdi—all made music integral to their success. Perhaps the most important event in the history of Christmas music was the introducing, by St. Francis of Assisi in the thirteenth century, of the "crib" or *præsepe* as a stimulus to visual religion: and one cannot doubt that the aural impetus was too important to neglect at a time when music, too, was blossoming, or at least budding. By 1400 we are coming to a firm path, after some two hundred and fifty years' walk on unsure ground before. Then, by 1650, as far as carols are concerned, we slip back into the Slough of Despond.

For the carol is the main artistic expression of the joy and delight of the common people for the birth of Christ—and one must not forget the spring and Easter carols, similarly and openly loving the seasons of the year.* The waits, such close cousins with the carol, are lesser in the family tree. The music of the masters, in celebration of Christmas, comes third in our survey of Christmas music. The carol stands supreme.

The word "carol," like the entire folklore of Christmas, is both obscure and complicated in its meanings and origins. "Gambol," wrote Sir Walter Scott, and he was as right as he could be: for to "carol" means to dance as well as to sing, and it appears (from the *Oxford English Dictionary*) to mean to dance in a ring as well. Though David danced before the Ark, the Reformation Churches have frowned on dancing as a religious act. Yet we constantly sing, in our most austere churches, carols, the rhythm of which demands that the feet

*The tune of "Good King Wenceslas" is really an Easter carol.

should tap, and asks that they should spring. Could there be a clearer dance tune than this?

Ex. III*

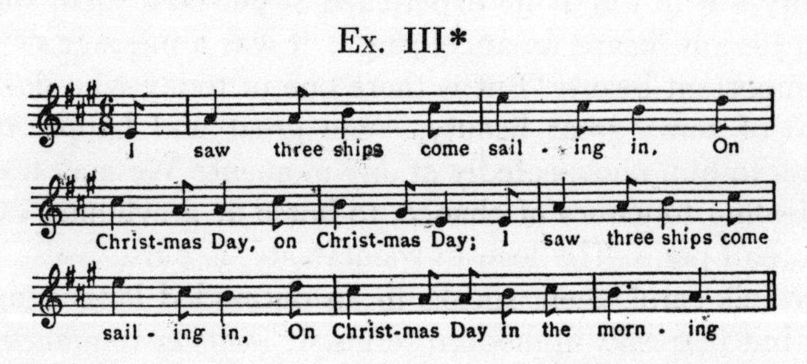

That lilting rhythm is very familiar in the real carols, and tells us more surely than the learned researchers can that the origin of the carol was the people dancing in their personal worship.

This music is essentially "popular" music, not in the sense in which we have learnt to use the word since Johann Strauss, but in the true sense of "the music of the people." We now divide music into water-tight compartments—"popular," "classical," "modern" music. But the carol is both "popular" and "modern": popular in the sense of people's own music, made by them for themselves, and modern in the sense of expressing an immediate, not a past, emotion.

The point is important. When a carol singer says—

"Joseph and Mary walked
Through an orchard good,
Where was cherries and berries
So red as any blood"

he is thinking only partly of the Nativity, and for the rest is thinking of his own home and the sloes or whins, the plums or raspberries, of his own village—of his own father or elder brother or uncle, in the mysterious past that happened some thirty years before. He is not an antiquarian. Joseph, an old man "when he wedded Mary in the land of Galilee," is one of the

*By courtesy of Novello & Co. Ltd.

associates of his lifetime. And we, singing the bird-song hundreds of years later, can, if we are alive, recapture that spirit, not in memory but in the living experience of our own small span of years. Joseph "heard an angel sing": it was a message of great and important beauty. But is there one of today who does not dream of some great beauty, some great and happy vision, coming to him unexpectedly at any moment? We may transfer that feeling to games of chance, to horse or greyhound racing, or football pools. The loss, in spontaneity, is ours.

The folk-carol, then, speaks in an outmoded language, perhaps, but it speaks in modern terms. It is never reminiscent of the joys which "with age diminish." The carol lives with us today as fresh, as new, if we accept it in its simplicity. That simplicity does not lack culture or "background." Indeed, the carols are highly picturesque in their imagery. The "Coventry Carol":

"Herod, the King
In his raging,
  Charged he hath this day
His men of might
In his own sight
  All young children to slay."

Or perhaps this verse:

"Then there was with the angel
  An host incontinent
Of heavenly bright soldiers,
  Which from the Highest was sent."

And for a more literal third example:

"Our wassail cup is made
  Of the rosemary tree,
And so is your beer
  Of the best barley."

Joseph's orchard was his, and ours, and so too are the corporeal heavenly host; and the beer and rosemary came from our gardens, if we still have them. The carols are modern; it is we who, in this civilized age, are out of date.

Above all, the carol has for its essential element a native joy in worship, a positive and infectious hilarity. Hilarious joy has by no means always been a concomitant of the Christian Church. A fear of formalism, of rites, of an encroaching worldliness and even paganism, together with a marked cleavage between northern and southern ideals of personal religion, have tended since the Golden Age of poetry and music to close the doors of the churches against the brighter-coloured forms of beauty. The splendours of the *design* of Gothic architecture, its cold magnificence, have led us, partly under Ruskin's influence, to forget that those austere arches and vaulted stone roofs were intended to bear brilliant colours. The tomb in Boxgrove Church, Sussex, so realistically restored, gives the right sense of the balance of paint and stone. I could not help thinking, as I wrote that, of Sir Henry Hadow's opening sentence to one of his best essays.* He writes: "Heine tells us the story of the monks of Basle who walked one evening in their monastery garden and heard a nightingale sing with such ravishing sweetness that they exorcised it." The carol was exorcised, too, and has never wholly returned except in revivals. For myself, at Christmas I want more people to be like Haydn, who "worshipped God in a cheerful temper," and who in his gayest moments of *The Creation* felt he was "never so pious as when I was composing this work; I knelt down daily and prayed God to strengthen me for it."

But, though we can hear in many carols the fresh laughter of spontaneous delight, the story of the Nativity is told always with reverence and with grave human detail, and there are carols of repentance and exhortation, like "Remember Adam's fall, O thou man."

*"The Place of Beauty in Worship" (*Collected Essays*, Hadow: Oxford).

No one, I am happy to think, can name an ultimate date of birth for a folk-tune. "Greensleeves" had been long enough known to Shakespeare's audience for him to quote it in his plays. So that accepting Dr. Percy Dearmer's view that "most of our carols were made during the two centuries and a half between the death of Chaucer in 1400 and the ejection of the Rev. Robert Herrick from his parish by Oliver Cromwell's men in 1647," we are still able to reach out fingers into the remotest past of men's memories before 1400, as we can dream back into incalculable ages of time gone when we read that "On Christmas night" was taken down in our lifetime from the singing of Mrs. Verrall, of Monks Gate, Sussex. We find the same dubiety in the principal source of our surviving old carols: Richard Hill's *Commonplace Book*. Apprentice and son-in-law to the grocer, John Wyngar, of the City of London, who was Lord Mayor in 1504, Hill seems to have had the mind of a literary jackdaw, noting in his diary poems and romances, extracts from Gower, tables and accounts, dates, recipes for dosing or cooking or brewing, lists of linen, family notes, hints for breaking horses, riddles, puzzles, verses, and carols. What a debt we owe to that hoarding ancient! Rural lore accounts for most of the other carols, with some printed versions from as far back as Wynkyn de Worde and a whole successive series of broadsheets. De Worde is evidence that carols go back farther than noted record, for it is unlikely he would waste his new craft on literary and religious experiment.

After two hundred years during which carols remained with the people, unofficial and secular expression of their Christmas joy frowned on by the Church, we come to the revival—to various collections of folk-verse and folk-music gathered by noble but humble clerics and scholars—Bishop Percy (of the *Reliques*), Sandys, Husk, Bramley, Neale, Helmore, and Stainer among others: and later by Cecil Sharp in his revival of English folksong.

Our texts are sometimes corrupt, edited, watered down, but

if we seek the sources with clear eyes, we can find the English carol.

The *Weinachtslieder* of Germany, the French *Noël,* Christmas songs in Czechoslovakia, Poland, and Russia, should not be forgotten, for they number many beautiful carols, which have, however, less freedom than our English ones.

The practice of walking the parish with suitable Christmas music had its origin in the pleasing custom of older times under which certain cities supplemented their watchmen and guards (for that is what "waits" first were) with a paid band of musicians. Grove's *Dictionary of Music and Musicians* reminds us that in "*Humphrey Clinker,* Matthew Bramble is welcomed to Bath by the Town Waits calling at his lodgings and playing." The word came to be applied also to the music played, and there survives from the eighteenth century a number of collections of such music, the "Chester Waits" and "London Waits" and the rest, among which are watchman's cries as well as dance tunes. But the custom spread to the unpaid Church musicians and lasted longer than Smollett's day, for Thomas Hardy in his *Under the Greenwood Tree* (1872), drawing upon his own and his father's memory, gives us what he has called "a rural painting of the Dutch school" of Tranter Dewey's choir and band at Mellstock in about the year 1820. "Barrel-organs"—those ancient mechanical players of a few set hymn tunes—had "come in terribly of late years," and with them in equal condemnation were classed clarinets—"clarinets, however, be bad at all times." The conservative rustic differed here from Mozart, but he had as healthy a regard for firm brass-line as ever Berlioz or Wagner had, for he clung to the leather-covered wind instrument, the serpent, predecessor of the ophicleide on which Mendelssohn makes Bottom bray in his *Midsummer Night's Dream* Overture. "Old things pass away, 'tis true," reflects Mr. Penny, the boot and shoe maker; "but a serpent was a good old note: a deep rich note was the serpent." And in performances of Mendelssohn today, we are fobbed off with a tuba.

Towards the common form that the continuation of itinerant carol-singing has taken, I confess I have little sympathy—the untrained, unorganized parties of begging children may show enterprise, but they have neither skill nor repertoire, neither joy in music nor sense of Christmas. Very much more could be done with walking carol-parties if the churches today would take a stronger interest in their music. The carol, perhaps for not wholly sound reasons, is still loved by the English people. The "carol service of nine lessons" has grown of late years into an annual event much looked forward to. I will put in a plea, however, that at Christmas-time, music in church should be kept as simple as possible, without display or elaboration, joyful, with much joining-in of the congregation, and simple, beautiful singing having full regard to the words.

Since Bramley and Stainer's *Christmas Carols Old and New* of 1871 brought the carol back into regular church use, as if they were ordinary hymns, most practitioners of church music, good, bad, and indifferent, professional and amateur, have tried their hands at writing carols. The amateur especially found the conventional hymn-carol, with its sentimental appeal and mistaken aims, "deplorably easy to write." In Hadow's words: "there has probably been no form of any art in the history of the world which has been so overrun by the unqualified amateur as English Church Music from about 1850 to about 1900." The change of heart began with the English revival in the 1880's, but only reached full fruition in Vaughan Williams' admirable collection of congregational Church music, *The English Hymnal* (1907).

This is not to condemn all the later carol tunes. Mendelssohn and Sir John Goss and Gustav Holst have added worthy carols to our better repertory. "We three Kings of Orient are" (1857) comes from as far as Williamsport, Pennsylvania. Vaughan Williams, Ireland, Martin and Geoffrey Shaw, Rubbra, and many others have written beautiful carols, and I incline to think that in "A Spotless Rose" Herbert Howells has touched a height of beauty rarely attained in English music since the days of William Byrd. But they lack the open-airness of the folk-carol, the sunlight of simplicity, the spontaneity of immediate joy. Of the more elaborate Christmas songs, the set by Peter Cornelius, the "Three Carols" for chorus and orchestra by Peter Warlock, and Arnold Bax's four pieces hold different but equivalent niches in my own affections, and many have lately loved singing Benjamin Britten's *Ceremony of Carols* for treble voices and harp.

Of the works designed by the earlier composers to celebrate or describe Christmas, that which has the warmest place in the English heart is the "Pastoral Symphony" from Handel's *Messiah.* We do not know so well the even more beautiful "Pastoral Symphony" from Bach's *Christmas Oratorio,* perhaps because of the difficulties inherent in the plan of the complete work. For it is not, though so entitled by the composer, a true oratorio, but a collection of Church Cantatas, telling the Gospel narrative ("with lyrical commentary," adds Terry) in six parts, to be sung successively at the services on Christmas Day, the two following days, the Feast of the Circumcision and the Sunday after, and the Feast of the Epiphany (1734-5). Even if performed on two occasions, this music seems to find itself cramped for space, but our Church is not that of Leipzig, and if we wish (as we ought) to know the work—one of the finest Bach wrote—we must accept the compromise of the concert hall.

Haydn's "Christmas" Symphony (No. 26) bears also the nickname of "Lamentations" and seems more suited to Advent solemnity than Christmas rejoicing. Corelli gives us a "Christmas Eve" concerto, there is Christmas music by Mendelssohn, Spohr, and Elgar, and Vaughan Williams beside his "Fantasia on Christmas Carols" has written a "quodlibet" on Christmas tunes to a ballet based upon Dickens' *Christmas Carol.* An entrancing but neglected work is Berlioz's oratorio, *L'Enfance du Christ,* in three parts, to a libretto of his own writing. It contains, perhaps, some of the loveliest and tenderest Christmas music ever written, as well as a strong dramatic and pictorial power.

For Christmas music is the simple expression of the people's joy, and to live in our hearts and not only in our minds, it must be direct, pertinent, bearing the best marks of tradition, yet spontaneous and free of utterance. There is ample music, and to spare, of the right quality and character, a character fully suggested by those lines written in 1546:

"Then, dear Lord, for thy great grace,
Grant us the bliss to see thy face,
Where we may sing to thy solace."

Celestial beauty, we know from the whole history of mankind, is more nearly attained by simplicity than by complication of utterance.

Some Great Nativity Pictures

by CELANDINE KENNINGTON

HE face of Helen of Troy, it is said, launched a thousand ships of war; it is certain that the face of Mary of Nazareth has inspired countless thousands of works of art. From about the tenth to the sixteenth century the Virgin and Child was the lodestar which drew the imagination and skill of the best artists. Backed by the fervent faith of the men and women of their age, and made possible by rich and powerful patrons, great masterpieces like a Coronation of the Virgin, the *Gozzoli* frescoes in Florence or *Michelangelo's* Sistine Chapel were achieved. The believer-artist in an age of unfaith can send the single trumpet-call of his own convictions ringing against the silent dark; but he cannot attain the full orchestral power of, say, *Fra Angelico,* who so obviously voiced the spirit of his age. To attain his full stature in religious art he must feel himself the confident mouthpiece of his time, not the voice of one crying in the wilderness.

I have been looking at some of these nativities lately, thinking about the kind of men who painted them, and the times they lived in. What did they want to convey, why did it all happen?

I suppose it began with a man of deep faith whose intensity of feeling impelled him to express his sense of wonder, of beauty, and of miracle. It had to manifest itself, or he would have perished. He was in happy relationship with others of his church. There were the bare walls to work on; he could make pigments and brushes; and colours and shapes were to him things of immense spiritual power. So the long procession started and soon produced some of the most moving and beautiful works of art we have ever known—the great Greek frescoes of the eighth century; the immense and impressive mosaics of the eleventh and twelfth; the golden glories of *Cimabue* and *Duccio;* the strong spring tides in Italy of the *Cinquecento;* on to *Giotto* and the full flood of the Renaissance.

Then came the ebb. There was a recurring wave in the seventeenth century in Spain—*El Greco* and *Murillo.* And then a receding tide which left only an occasional lovely sea pool in the dry sands; a *Blake,* a *Burne-Jones,* an *Eric Gill.*

What is specially interesting is the wide difference in the pictures, according to the man, his country and his time. They put so much of themselves into these pictures; the kind of clothes they admired, the dogs they loved. *Dürer* uses village types for his favourite knights on caracoling horses and quite without irrelevance. It is curious how often ruined architecture or broken masonry forms the framework of the picture; far too often for it to be a necessity of the design. Is it part of an accepted symbolism whose key we have lost; does it typify the passing away of the old order and the fulfilling of the promise "and behold I make all things new"? The scene varies widely: it can be a barn, a ruined palace, or a thatched hut. The Madonna may be a stout Flemish matron presenting her sturdy boy with a complacent air, or the fragile wonderstruck girl of *El Greco,* holding the Baby's wrappings with the utmost delicacy lest the marvel take flight by rough handling. But all these differences are over-arched by an underlying sense of spiritual unity, of wonder and of miracle. All barriers of time and space are effaced. The childlike faith of the thirteenth-century Italian and the mature reasoning of the sixteenth-century Fleming are merged in the light which streams from the manger at Bethlehem.

*Mr. Berensen speaks of a mysterious "something existent in a picture beyond its immediate subject" which he calls the

**Sandro Boticelli* by Yukio Yashiro (The Medici Society).

"overmeaning." "For it is probably over and beyond what the artist himself had in mind and certainly what he could hope to convey with precision." Of that there is no doubt. Mr. Berensen continues: "For the overmeaning is due to the fact that, be what may the immediate instrument of the artist, his ultimate instrument is the heart. And the heart is of a mechanism so subtle, so varied and so uncertain as to baffle any precise calculation of its working and to put it beyond the reach of accurate control." To be sensitive to the "overmeaning" of a picture takes us right into the heart of its painter.

EL GRECO (*Plate IV*)

El Greco's constant swinging shapes and interplay of elongated triangles build up his Madonna and Child into an unearthly magic with a strange feeling of elemental powers around them. A Spanish critic of a later day says of him "He had few pupils. None cared to follow his capricious extravagant style which was suitable only to himself." Happily for him, and us. When we know what we endure from the protruding arms and legs of the "school" of *Michelangelo,* think what we would suffer from a school of *El Greco!* But St. Theresa, his contemporary, says of him: "I see a white and a red of a quality as one finds nowhere in nature, for they shine more brightly than the colours we perceive; and I see pictures as no painter has yet painted, whose models one finds nowhere in nature; and yet they are nature itself and life itself, and the most perfect beauty imaginable."

FRA ANGELICO (*Plate III*)

I find *Fra Angelico* one of the most moving of artists. He is blessedly unaware of non-essentials, and a pure glow of praising God rises from all his pictures. He is early enough in date to be gloriously free from troublesome discoveries like perspective, and he has a sense of the spiritual power of pure delicate colour that has never been surpassed. Blue, rose, lilac, green, are dreams of ethereal loveliness, and his golden embroideries are never heavy but like a delicate filigree of sunlight. And his oneness: look at the utter devotion of the kings in his picture, they are wrapt in wonder of what they are beholding; there are no distractions. *Fra Angelico's* world is in the heavenly sphere, no architecture, or dogs, or other irrelevancies; flowers he loves and paints tenderly, but primarily as a means of gilding his grass, not for themselves. It is strange how in this picture the grille background does not make us feel confined, but gives us a great promise of a superbly glorious beyond.

REMBRANDT (*Plate I*)

The *Rembrandt* is a complete contrast. *Rembrandt* who was wealthy and at one period of his life a collector of armour and curios, a great and extravagant man of the world; yet when thinking of the birth of Christ goes straight back to the big barn at his father's mill.

It is one of the pictures that takes us completely into itself; we are part of it. We ourselves stand or kneel in the outer circle round that central wonder of wonders. The little boy, so devout, and yet with a thought to spare that his beloved dog should behave reverently too, he is our little boy, our nephew, our grandchild. The light of the world; "It" is our light too.

Has ever a more beautiful figure been painted than the standing shepherd? Note his dignity, his power; a lifetime of faithful work is finding its culmination and reward in this experience. Very simple traveller kings crowd the doorway, but it is the shepherd's hour. Is Mary a portrait of his beautiful dead wife, and is the scene reminiscent of the wonder of his own first-born? All human tenderness seems packed into this picture, as well as an ineffable sense of the godhead made incarnate.

Although everything centres round the radiant Baby, the uprights and rafters of the barn take our minds further. The

Courtesy of The Medici Society Ltd., London

ADORATION OF THE SHEPHERDS

VAN RYN REMBRANDT, 1606—1669 National Gallery, London

Plate I

Courtesy of The Medici Society Ltd., London

THE NATIVITY

ALESSANDRO BOTTICELLI, 1444—1510 National Gallery, London

Plate II *Page 126*

Courtesy of The Medici Society Ltd., London

ADORATION OF THE MAGI

FRA ANGELICO, 1387—1455 San Marco, Florence

Courtesy of The Medici Society Ltd., London

ADORATION OF THE SHEPHERDS

EL GRECO, 1545—1614

prophecy of the crucifixion is there; among those dark beams we can sense the cross; the leaning ladder is already in place for the descent. The shadows hold a deeper shadow of the future; the crib is overshadowed by Calvary. This is so great a picture that there is very little to say about it. It is an experience.

BOTTICELLI (*Plate II*)

In the *Botticelli* nativity we have something that cannot be looked at as an ordinary picture, for it is much more than that. It is the chart of a man's soul, the full confession of his faith. He whose mind up till his conversion rejoiced in lovely rhythmic pagan figures, he whose sense of selection was so impeccable, and whose design was so sensitive and so daring, puts everything into this picture regardless of all artistic canons. He wants to give us all the wonder and richness of the Christianity that Savonarola awoke in him; he can leave nothing out, he must tell everything, whether it makes a picture or whether it doesn't. This nativity was painted a few years after Savonarola had been burned at the stake, and *Botticelli* had been devoting much time to collecting evidence to clear his master's memory of the charges brought against him. It is specially significant not only for the words of political prophecy on the gold scroll, but for being the only picture *Botticelli* ever signed. Doesn't this mean it is something intensely personal—something with which he wants us to identify him?

It is in four very distinct layers almost equal in size: the golden firmament, a strata of earthly upper air; a layer containing all the principal figures, and at the bottom a scene of men and angels which is almost another picture in itself.

What impresses me most is the complete change in the personality of the Madonna. His earlier ones, however lovely, have a curious inward-turning look, a sort of absorbed ecstasy, that can be entirely selfish. All his principal figures have it. Venus rising from the sea has a sad, and utterly fey expression;

his Spring broods over her own condition; the Venus, of his Mars and Venus, dreams of her moments of love, unheeding the naughty pranks that the baby fauns around her are playing with her warrior's armour. But the Madonna of this nativity bends in utter selflessness to the Child, her whole being is an outpouring of her love and devotion to him. No self remains. She sums up all that his conversion must ultimately have meant to *Botticelli.* Its freedom from personal satisfaction, its wholeness, its singleness, its peace. Peace is the picture's *leitmotif.* Everywhere are lovely olive branches; it is peace from on high for angelic messengers bear them, and are filled with a tender solicitude for the humans; how eagerly they are ushering in the kings and the shepherds! One is even gently turning a shepherd's head into the right direction, to be sure he misses nothing of the marvellous event.

The traditional cave motive is faithfully embarked upon, but is broken into, as if half-way through *Botticelli* simply couldn't stand its gloom and its coldness. So he breaks it with one of his very favourite *motifs,* light shining between the trunks of trees heavy with foliage. It makes the cave into a very draughty habitation, and robs it of any sense of even gloomy cosiness, and all sense of security is gone. Does he mean the warm inside of Mary's cloak to be the real security; love and not stones offer the precious infant shelter; his must be a home not made with hands. Joseph sits crouched by the Child in an attitude of passionate attention, and the ass, breathing heavily, looks down with a grave expression as if sensing for his kind a future connection with a triumph which ended in a tragedy. The figures of the shepherds and the Magi are not made important in themselves, indeed it is hard to distinguish the one from the other. They, with their eager angelic guides are all swung into a rhythmic circle surrounding the central figures. This section of the picture is so complete in itself that it is often reproduced alone.

The next layer consists of sky, a band of trees and the thatched roof of the little hut which forms a penthouse over the front of the cave. On this roof sit three angels reading from a large book. I feel they are meant to form a link between mankind and the floating angels above; are they translating the celestial singing into words possible for human ears?

The top of the picture is the golden empyrean filled with the heavenly host, singing and praising God. Partly against pure gold, partly against blue sky, they float with unimaginable ease and grace, some of the most lovely figures that have ever been painted. They seem to need the weight of the swinging crowns to keep them within our sight at all. Although there are only twelve, they give us a great sense that there are many more just out of sight. I feel these angels voice for *Botticelli* his freedom, his certainty, his ecstasy. His pagan forms are invested with a rich new life, and their highest meaning has been found.

In the bottom section of the picture he gives us three olive-crowned humans and three angels carrying olive branches and approaching to caress them. There is an awkwardness about the figures that must be intentional, as *Botticelli* was such a supreme master of grace. A sense that the human figures are almost wrestling before being able to receive the caresses of their angels, a sense of the struggle it is to humanity to accept the divine. Or is it a faintness from battling with the very vital little devils that have just been forcibly cast out? These leave the issue in no doubt as they grimace and spit a last ineffectual jet of poison while scuttling to hide in the rocks.

Botticelli has used the natural stratification of these rocks to separate this scene from the central one, and has also made the figures considerably smaller as if to emphasize that this episode is of vastly less importance than the mother and child.

This is a picture about which there has been much controversy and which has received many harsh words from critics. Its small size, curiously unpictorial composition and rather dim colour make it terribly disappointing at first sight, especially as it hangs beside the artistically flawless pagan Mars and

Venus. But when we look deeply into it, and into the artist's life we can see why the Japanese critic Yukio Yashiro described it as "that mystic nativity, the gem of all the *Botticellis* in the world."

These pictures are a few gems selected from the fabulous wealth of the Middle Ages. Where are the nativities of today? There are few. We commission murals of shipbuilding yards and factory scenes, and very fine they can be. Artists paint company directors, and sunlit nudes; they paint landscapes, lobsters, jugs, bananas—never a nativity or a Virgin and Child. Even in their rightful domain—the Christmas card—nativities have almost been ousted by saucy robins or snowy coaching scenes.

But there are signs of the dawning of a new age of faith. A beautifully constructed crib has appeared in our local church, the work of a neighbouring artist-craftsman; the demand for nativity plays is constant and increasing. On a Suffolk farm the men and landgirls were rehearsing a Christmas tableau; they accidentally left the door open, and found they had drawn in all the home-going villagers. It really was the shepherds come to worship that time.

So we see that a spirit is moving over the face of the dark waters which can bring artists who will surpass *Cimabue* and *Raphael.* Man will bring with him to his creative work not only the seeds of inspiration, but the harvest of the ages of reason and scientific achievement.

Then there will dawn a new golden age with the glow of the newly risen sun outshining the glitter of the cold coins of materialism.

It Happened at Christmas

by PETER HOWARD

CHRISTMAS is the time for ghosts. Some folk do not believe in ghosts, because they have never seen one. Well, lots of people have never seen the United States of America, but they believe in them just the same.

A year or two ago at Christmas I had a strange experience. You might like to hear about it. It was over in a few minutes yet its effects have lasted until today.

I must tell you that I am not a superstitious or credulous fellow. By nature I am cynical and suspicious. Seven years' experience of the Black Craft of Fleet Street as political commentator and leader writer taught me never to take men at their own evaluation and always to test events in the balance of my own mind.

My attitude to Christmas was that of nine-tenths the rest of us. I do not remember my first Christmas on this earth, being but five days old at the time. But I remember many of those which followed it. The bulk and mystery of the stocking in the early darkness of Christmas morning stands out sharply. I used to borrow my father's largest stocking and hang it empty on the end of my bed the night before. Then somehow during the night it got filled with knobbly parcels—a festoon of crackers to decorate the tip and the inevitable orange in the toe.

I knew that a magic and benevolent old gentleman named Father Christmas used to pop down the chimney while I was asleep, to perform this miracle. I used to send letters to him a week or so before Christmas telling him what I wanted. And the letters must have been delivered, for my requests were almost always granted.

Father Christmas came in his magic sledge drawn by eight flying reindeer and down the chimney into my nursery he floated, without getting soot in his beard and with snow from the North Pole still upon his boots.

I loved the presents he brought me, but to tell you the truth I would have been scared to death to see him in my bedroom. What kept me awake on Christmas Eve was not a desire to see Father Christmas, which was my mother's theory, but a terror lest I should not get to sleep in time and should be caught awake when that mysterious apparition with the large sack appeared feet foremost through the fireplace.

Then, when I was almost eight, a horrid little redheaded friend of mine told me that there was no such person as Father Christmas, that it was only my Father and Mother making some sort of a game of me.

I hated him and tried to hit him. For by instinct I knew that what he said was true. He sat down on the heap of coke in our backyard by which he was standing when he gave me this information, and then ran off blubbing, as we called it.

All mystery and wonder departed from Christmas for me then. But not the pleasure. I still liked the crinkly parcels in the stocking. Christmas became for me a time when I received a lot of nice presents. True, Church was mixed up with it all somehow. We went to church on Christmas Day, with a stiff collar sawing at my neck. But I never fully understood why. Anyway, the turkey and plum pudding tasted all the better when we got home.

As I grew to what is called man's estate the stream of presents which relatives and friends used to send me at Christmas was suddenly diverted towards my younger brother. "He's more the age for presents, isn't he, dear?" I did not like this. I had a shrewd suspicion that my relatives meant that he would be satisfied with gifts of a kind and cost that no longer satisfied me. But I had other consolations.

I knew where to obtain Christmas spirit. It came out of a bottle and cost 12s. 6d. a time, though I believe it is now up to 27s. 6d. Christmas was a time when we all spent a bit more than we could afford, ate a bit more and drank a bit more than we could digest—and to hell with the hangover. That was something for the New Year to worry about. And it usually solved the problem by another party. Then another, on a slightly smaller scale. Then another. In the City I believe they call this the law of diminishing returns.

I still looked forward to Christmas, though not so much as I had done as a child. And sometimes, when it actually arrived, I found it a bit of a strain and bore.

Then I was asked by some friends to the Christmas party where my strange experience befell me. From what I have told you, you can guess the frame of mind in which I went, expecting the usual clatter of bottles and talk, the usual mixture of soft eyes and hard drink.

When I got inside the house, my friends said to me "Come and look at the crib." I scarcely remembered what a crib was, so I went to see. There at the foot of the stairs, under a huge Christmas tree which towered up into the darkness beyond the first landing, was set out the model of a village. It was illuminated by candles. Its beauty caught your heart.

There was the manger and in it lay the baby Jesus, watched over by Mary and Joseph, while an ox and an ass warmed Him with their breath. Scores of little pathways led to the manger from the village. They were cut through the moss which formed the fields. They wound between lakes made of looking-glass, cascades and waterfalls of silver paper, and snowdrifts made of flour.

And up these pathways hurried hundreds of people, all going in the same direction and all bearing gifts to the manger.

My friends told me this crib came from Provence in the South of France, where at Christmas-time most people set one up in their houses. Certainly these figures were lifelike. You could almost see them move and hear the swish and rustle of their colourful Provençal garments.

There was the French mayor with his tricolor scarf of office around his middle and a huge umbrella, hurrying along with an address of welcome.

There was the baker carrying crisp, brown, curly loaves of French bread.

The fisherman, with dark-blue jersey and red-bobbined cap, had a skip of mullet, turbot and lobsters on his shoulders.

And there, hobbling along with one hand on the shoulder of a little boy and the other groping his way in front of him, went the blind man of the village. The blind man was the only one of all those hurrying towards the manger who did not carry a present with him. "He has nothing in this world," my friends told me, "so he is taking himself to Jesus as an offering."

Among the crowd were the three Kings from the East, Melchior with an ermine cloak and bearing a box of gold—Caspar with purple robes and lifting a casket of frankincense high in the air as he strode up the hillside—Balthasar with a crown of jewels upon his head and going humbly along the pathway on his knees, carrying his offering of myrrh. With them were their servants leading an elephant which carried their luggage on its back.

From a little attic window above the manger itself, a boy with his arms thrown up in the air in astonishment looked out at the crowds streaming up the hill towards him. "Who is he?" I asked my friends. Then they told me of another age-old legend from the Ardennes in Provence.

It is said that on the night Jesus was born, a village boy, somewhat soft in the head, who had nowhere else to sleep, was sent into the chaff-loft above the manger. He had no idea of the events that were happening down below while he slept. But when he looked out of the loft window early in the morning, he saw all the people hurrying towards him up the hill. So he flung his arms up in the astonishment which his poor bemused brain felt. And ever after he had the power of healing in his hands and a look of far-away serenity and certainty in his eyes, though he never spoke again.

I looked at all those people hurrying up the hillside together, people of every class and colour united by their love of the Baby in the manger, with one heart and one mind because they were on the give, not on the get. A world in miniature with the answer to all the problems of the world. So clearly and simply set out under that Christmas tree in my friend's home—all men travelling the same road because they had one shared, selfless and sacrificial objective.

I felt even my old journalist's leathery heart, tanned and pickled to hardness by the years as it had been, stir and turn within me. I said to my friends rather hurriedly: "It's pretty, isn't it? What a pity it is not all true."

We went in to supper. With the food and conversation the spell of the crib lifted from me. I began to crack jokes, to argue with my neighbours and to trade in the gossip of the town, which at that time gave me my daily bread.

But afterwards we returned to the tree and sat around it. The candles on it gave us our only illumination. They were living things, like tiny, shining swords among the dark evergreen of the branches. The figures of the crib took on colour and warmth and even movement, as the topmost candles in the dark tree stirred and swayed in the draught above the staircase landing.

It may have been my imagination that the three Wise Kings had moved nearer to the manger than they were before supper. Surely Melchior had been behind the baker? Whereas now he was level with the farmer and past the little fountain at the corner of the road. But I dismissed such foolish thoughts from my mind. We sang the old carols together:

"O little town of Bethlehem
How still we see thee lie!
Above thy deep and dreamless sleep
The silent stars go by.
Yet in thy dark street shineth
The everlasting Light.
The hopes and fears of all the years
Are met in thee tonight.

What can I give Him
Poor as I am?
If I were a shepherd
I would bring a lamb.
If I were a wise man
I would do my part.
Yet what I can, I give Him—
Give my heart."

Presently the candles on the tree started to flicker and burn out one by one. We sat in silence watching them. And I began to turn over in my mind the tragedy that two thousand years after the simple and costly idea of loving your neighbour as yourself was brought into this world, we should see things as they are today—teeming millions of humanity bending their wealth, strength and ingenuity to the single task of Number One first.

How different history might have been, I thought, if the leaders of nations were stirred by the spirit of the crib to some other ambition than personal power and national expansion.

I began to list in my mind the people I would like to see transformed in nature to the simplicity, selflessness and love of those who were still hurrying up the hillside towards the manger. It was a long list, though my own name did not appear on it. It started in the ranks of my home circle, included many of the men I worked with in Fleet Street each day, and indeed it embraced the majority of all I knew, especially the politicians.

And suddenly, with only one candle left alight on that tree, and with myself and my friends sitting in silence below, there was a stir and change in the whole atmosphere of the place. I became conscious of some Power, almost of some Presence there which had not been before. It was as real as revolution. You could find it all around you. It was almost as though a voice were speaking to me.

"How can you help a world that is as selfish as hell, if you are as selfish as hell yourself?" this voice said to me.

"But I am not selfish," I answered in my heart, very shocked and surprised. "I am no more selfish than my neighbours and a good bit less so than most of them."

"Your money, your future, your security, your comfort—aren't these the things you worry about most?" said the voice. "You are indifferent to most of the people you know, and are critical of those you do not actively dislike. You want to see so many other people different. But there is one place only where you can make a start."

I thought to myself: "Yes. If everybody used Christmas as a time to end for ever their grievances and resentments, it would be more like that village with the crib." And instantly, so clear and loud that I looked around me to see whether my friends had heard it too, the voice said: "Why not apologize to your wife? Why not get honest with her, too?"

Every instinct in me rebelled against this suggestion, as we sat there under the tree. I got along well enough with Doe. We agreed perfectly, so long as I got my own way. We were much happier than many of the other young couples we knew. An occasional row added salt to life. As for honesty, Doe knew all about me—except the things I felt would make her think less of me if she heard them.

Yet again and again I heard that voice say to me: "Apologize to your wife. Get honest with her."

And I knew I would have to do it. I decided I would do it.

At that moment, a chemical change took place in me. There, in the darkness beside the crib, under that Christmas tree, sitting in silence with my friends, I felt the whole organization of my body alter. It was as much of a felt experience as the warmth of a fire or the cold of a wind.

Suddenly peace and love came into a heart where restlessness and criticism had ruled before. I felt myself made different.

Then I noticed a curious physical fact. I could still see the Baby in the manger, the figures hurrying up the hill, the outline of the tree and the faces of my friends. Yet the last candle in the tree had flickered out some time before.

Maybe my eyes had grown accustomed to the darkness, though I have never been able to see in it so clearly before or since. Maybe.

That night I knelt and prayed beside my bed. It was many Christmasses since I had done so, and the last time had been at my mother's knee.

In the hard world of the following day, I found it difficult to apologize to Doe for the coldness of the years and to tell her of the secrets in my heart, the sort of man I really was, not the man she thought me. But I did so.

That talk brought new unity and warmth into our whole married life. It gave us the miracle of a new home together.

A new happiness and a new love for mankind was born in my heart and has grown there ever since. "A new heart also will I give you and a new spirit will I put within you: and I will take away the stony heart out of your flesh and I will give you a heart of flesh."

There is a supernatural Power available at Christmas for those who care to accept it.

It is the only force which can make the new world of our dreams come true. For it alone is powerful enough to eliminate the massed greeds, fears and hatreds which wrecked our old world.

The spirit of the Child can turn the tide of materialism. Some may not believe in it—but it is unrationed for all to avail themselves of it. Invisible as electricity, universal as light, it is the one force today able to cure the chaos of the world as man has made it.

It is the strongest Power in creation and the one which at the moment we know least about. The greatest discoveries of our age and generation may be in the realm of that supernatural power.

The World Rejoices

CANADA * SYRIA * HOLLAND
AUSTRALIA * FRANCE * NIGERIA

A Festival of Family—Canada (SIMONE VUIGNIER)

AT ELEVEN at night on Christmas Eve off we drive. We go each year like this to midnight mass—driving in the horse sleigh, through the woods heavy with snow. Many folk drive five or six miles to be there. Outside the church becomes a great social rendezvous. Everyone shouts greetings as we climb from the sleighs and the men tie up the horses.

From the frosty night we step into the warmth of the church. The service is a wonderfully rich experience, with its lovely singing and all the candles and lights.

Then out into the blue night again around two o'clock, and into the sleigh once more, muffling up in furs. There are no lights on the sleighs and the reins are left loose, for the horses know their way. The bells jingle on the night air and the sleigh-runners crunch through the deep, new snow. There's nothing in the world quite so exhilarating as this night drive beneath the starry sky and between the white trees—singing carols all the way home. You feel like in fairyland. A wonderful way to start Christmas!

Back home a huge, crackling fire awaits you. And the women who've stayed behind have lit the candles on the tree and laid out the presents and made ready the great meal. I run up and wake the children, and when they come down the presents are given and we all gather round the table. The special feature of the meal is *tourtières,* lovely meat pies, made a week before and frozen to keep. Now they're piping hot before us. After the meal we again sing and then around 4 a.m. it's time for bed.

When we get up again, around eleven, we go off in the sleigh and call on uncles and aunts. I often feel that the unity of the family is the thing that French-speaking Canada has especially to give the world; and Christmas above all others is the family time. All members of the family call on each other on Christmas Day and the days following, and jealousies and misunderstandings are swallowed up in the festive spirit. The meals are tremendous affairs. Often when you're invited out you find your hosts have asked all their family and friends, and fifty of you sit down to table—or eat in shifts if there's not room for all at once!

On New Year's morn comes the culmination of all this family time: the *bénédiction paternelle.* The family gathers in the home of the grandfather. The children are all there, even the very youngest. When all are assembled, the eldest son goes to his father and asks for his blessing on the whole family. Everyone kneels and Grandpa asks God to bless the family for the rest of the year.

* * * * *

Christmas Bonfires—Syria (FREYA STARK)

Najla, my landlady, and Elias the carpenter, were Syriac Christians from Diarbekr, and belonged to that part of the sect which Rome has gathered into its fold, without altering many of the old customs and ritual. Near Christmas-time Najla told me that they were going to read the Gospel out in the court by a bonfire on Christmas Eve, as every family does—and would I join in the ceremony?

I was going out that evening, and dressed a little earlier, and found the two small boys, Jusuf and Charles, waiting on my doorstep, their feelings equally divided between the splendour of my appearance in evening dress and the excitement of a bonfire. They took me one by each hand into the open court, where small lanterns were hanging among red and green paper streamers, and a heap of dry thorns stood in one corner.

"The youngest should read, but Charles knows only his ABC," said Najla while she handed us candles, "so it will be Jusuf. May the Holy Words bring you all your heart's desire, O Light of my Eyes!" She kissed me, and after her the two children came up shyly and lifted their cheeks to be kissed, while Elias with the tarbush pushed back off his fine old aquiline grizzled face, smiled upon us all.

Then Jusuf, who is ten, read out the Gospel, standing very straight with the lighted candle in his hand, his face full of seriousness, an impressive little figure under the stars. There was no wind; the candle flames burned clear and still. The four walls shut out everything except the motionless tops of the palm trees in surrounding groves. The outer gate was locked and barred, in memory no doubt of many persecutions. In the childish Arabic, the old story came with a new and homely grace; and we listened, moved and silent, standing like living altars, holding our lighted candles. Then Elias bent down with a match to the fire; the children clutched my arm in excitement, "Watch how it burns!" said Najla; for the luck of the house depends on it. The match went out.

Elias tried again—a little flame flickered and hesitated; Najla, resourceful, denied the tenets of predestination and poured paraffin on the strategic point; and the fire leaped to a blaze. It lit the children's oval faces with their long dark lashes, and Najla's long plaits with kerchief tied above them. The four voices joined in some old native psalm; and the flame of the fire rising so straight into the quiet sky, made one think of yet earlier worships, of Abel and Abraham and Isaac; and older than these, for presently, when the thorns were but red embers, Najla took my hand and made me leap thrice across them, wishing my wish, as no doubt the Babylonian maidens did to the honour of their gods.

Next morning, at 4.30, when the minarets across the water scarce showed against the faintness of the dawn, my hostess and I were already on our way to Mass in the Syriac Church. The bridge of boats was deserted. The sentry, evidently a Christian also, gave poor Najla a palpitation by informing us that we should be late. Najla keeps her high heels and her walking for great occasions only, and they were a little unmanageable.

We reached the Christian quarter across the early silence of New Street, and entered dark alleys filled with streams of quiet people on their way to the Chaldean, Armenian, Latin, Syriac, or Jacobite churches, which are all hidden away unobtrusively among the labyrinth of houses. They are modern and ugly when seen in the vacant light of day, but now as we came from the half-light outside, we opened the heavy door on what looked like a bed of tulips brilliantly illuminated, so vivid and rustling and shimmering were the many-coloured silk izars of the women who filled the nave in the light of lamps and candles.

In the centre of the church, half hidden by the crowd, the Bishop and his clergy were busy over another bonfire, surrounded by men who chanted a wild swift Syriac hymn—the tongue in which legend says that Adam lamented over the death of Abel. The male congregation at the back kept up the humming monotone accompaniment which takes the place of an organ.

As we entered, the dry wood caught fire and a sheet of flame rose half-way to the ceiling. The silken hoods round us rustled like a field of barley in a breeze. The Bishop, in a robe of cream and gold and crimson, his mitre high above the congregation, took in his arms a figure of the Infant Christ on a crimson cushion. Followed by his train, he walked slowly round the church, while a low canticle, wild no longer, but deep and grave and very touching rose from all sides where the men were standing. The women did not sing.

After this the service continued very like a Roman Catholic High Mass. The warmth, the unknown speech, the murmur of prayer, cast a rich drowsiness over me. The Bishop's gold shoes and crimson stockings; the embroidered crimson kerchief which hung from his wrist to the ground; his long auburn beard; the silk gauntlets, coloured like blood with the stigmata worked upon them in gold; the acolytes who held tall feather fans with tinkling ornaments upon them, all grew blurred in a dream. The Elevation awoke me; the bell rang, cymbals clashed, acolytes shook their fans till the ornaments rattled like dice boxes, and the rustle of the izars as the women rose to kneel was like a wave breaking softly.

Then the Bishop, bending over the altar rail, gave with his two joined hands the touch of Peace to a member of the congregation, who passed it on to the next, and so on from worshipper to worshipper, row after row, through the whole length of the church.

Soon after that, Mass was over. We crushed our way out into the narrow lane, and discovered that little Charles was lost. There was a hectic search, for the sense of danger is so inbred in the Eastern Christian that it enters in a surprising way into the least threatening moments of his life. But Charles was merely lost in his own meditations behind a pillar. He awoke to the ordinary facts of life when we stopped at the pastrycook's door to choose the Christmas cakes.

—From "Baghdad Sketches" (John Murray)

★ ★ ★ ★ ★

In the Land of Clogs—Holland (ANNELOU TEXEIRA DE MATTOS)

In Holland, Christmas celebrations are sharply divided between the sublime and the ridiculous. The light-hearted celebrations are kept to St. Nicholas' Day, the fifth of December, and the twenty-fifth is a more serious time of church-going and family visits.

On December 5th, St. Nicholas goes round traditionally on a white horse with a black servant in attendance. He is supposed to have come from Spain by boat and the servant is a blackamoor from Spain. He carries a huge sack of presents for good children and a birch to deal with naughty children. And if boys have been very naughty—little girls, of course, never are—rumour has it they will be put in that big bag and taken away to Spain.

St. Nicholas wears a bishop's red robe with a gold mitre and a long white beard. He listens down the chimneys to what the children say and has a large book in which he takes notes.

At my home a friend dresses up on the evening of December 5th as St. Nicholas. Accompanied by a black servant he comes into the children's parties. There he makes a little speech and discloses amazing inside knowledge of the latest naughtiness of the children—how little Piet should be better at going to bed, and the little Griet should help her mother more, and Jan should eat up his buttermilk pudding.

It is all very terrifying, and I remember to this day when I was six or seven and St. Nicholas invaded our party and suddenly asked me to recite a verse. I blushed purple and hid behind everyone. I remember he made his appearance in dramatic fashion. The door of the playroom opened a little, in came a black hand and threw a shower of nuts. "O there he is!" chorused all the children, and sure enough St. Nicholas came stalking in, followed by his faithful black servant who threw ginger nuts and sweets to everyone.

On St. Nicholas' Eve we do not hang up stockings, but put out "klompen," our wooden clogs, beside the chimney. Into the "klompen" the children put a little hay and some sugar for St. Nicholas' horse. Sure enough in the morning both hay and sugar are gone, so you know he has called. He leaves instead of presents gingerbread cakes made in the shapes of boys and girls, sometimes over two feet tall, or hearts made of sugar, something like fondant, in many colours, and marzipan in traditional shapes of sausages, hams, pigs' knuckles, and cheeses.

Half the fun of St. Nicholas' Day is that for weeks beforehand the whole family have been highly secretive, wrapping up presents with a great element of mystery. One of the many pranks we play on one another is to give very small gifts, and to wrap them up in dozens of packages one inside the other. You get an enormous parcel, undo wrapping after wrapping, and finally get to quite a tiny present. With it will be a poem giving home truths. It is all anonymous and you are not supposed to know who has given the present or written the poem. The poems are signed "Santa."

Other elements of mystery come in. There will be a loud ringing at your door. You go to answer it and find a package on the doorstep but no one there. No doubt it has come from a neighbour or a relation—or was it St. Nicholas? You never quite know.

So you have all the fun around December 5th. The twenty-fifth is the solemn time. At Christmas-time all the family gets together and goes to church together. Practically everyone goes to church at midnight on the twenty-fourth. At home they have Christmas trees with candles and sing Christmas songs. On the trees hang apples, oranges and nuts that you can eat. At eleven o'clock on Christmas morning, coffee and cake will be ready for visitors and relations who call. At midday there is a great family meal when Grandpa and the children all sit down together to eat a fine roast—rabbit or hare, or if lucky a goose or chicken.

* * * * *

Cobbers' Christmas—Australia (JIM COULTER)

"Hey, Bill, is it true that in your part of the world you go swimming on Christmas Day?"

"Sure we do—and have ice cream with our plum pudding. It's the middle of summer for us."

"What about the poultry? D'you have that cold?"

"Not on your life. Piping hot. With Mum herself just about roasted, with an outside temperature of a hundred or more, and much hotter in the kitchen."

Jack broke in: "Gosh! What does seem silly in looking back is the argument that we pick with our climate. Take Father Christmas for instance. All done up in red woollen stuff, complete with flowing white whiskers and wig, sitting in a bargain basement, while kids by the hundred whisper to him what presents they want. And all the time the poor old boy is pouring with perspiration."

Tony spoke up: "Christmas for us always fell plumb in the middle of the harvesting season—almost to a day. Wheat crops are tricky too. The longer you leave them the more risk of weevil and 'rust.' Besides, a chance fall of rain could flatten the whole crop. But all the same on every property around us the folk used to knock off for Christmas Day."

"That's the real Australia, but you can have it on your own for mine," said Ken. "We live right near the beach outside Brisbane, and used to have our roast chicken cold, with lettuce and tomatoes, under a beach umbrella on the sand. I reckon fruit salad is better than hot plum pudding any day."

"All you fellows think of is your stomachs," complained Fred. "But I think one of the most real memories I have of Christmas at home is 'carols by candlelight.' To me that's the Australian equivalent of the English house-to-house carol singing. Gee, I get a kick out of going along. There are a hundred thousand people there in the gardens and we all sing together, each reading the carols by the light of a candle. Some charity show gets a big haul that night, but you're only too glad to part for what you've had. There are whole families from Gran down to the youngsters, joining in the singing. I'm not sentimental, but it stirred me when I went. It was as though a hundred thousand people became one family for the evening."

* * * * *

The Children Celebrate—France (MARCELLE AUCLAIR)

In France, Christmas is children's time. Grown-ups have their gifts on the first of January. At Christmas it is the childrens' cup that overfloweth. Tradition dictates that on Christmas Eve, before going to bed, the children put their shoes in the fireplace. As soon as they are asleep their parents come in on tip-toe and lay toys, sweets and good things of all sorts around each pair of shoes. Christmas morning the children do not stay long in bed. The moment they wake up they dash to the hearth and shouts of surprise and joy fill the house.

Who is supposed to have delivered these wonderful gifts? In some of the families it is the Infant Jesus, in others Father Christmas. Mother and Father both say they have nothing to do with it. Till what age do the children believe in this miracle? Some, even up to seven or eight years of age, send off little letters in which they write down what they want for Christmas. Then, gravely, these letters are put in the pillar-box in an envelope addressed to "Little Jesus, Heaven."

Christmas trees are only popular in France in districts where fir trees grow—Alsace, the Vosges, the Jura. People in Paris have Christmas trees because Paris picks all the provincial customs she likes best and adopts them for herself. So on December 25th there are children's parties where songs and rounds are sung under a big fir tree.

There is also the adorable custom of the crib. This is generally in the children's room, on the mantelpiece; a little stable made of straw and light wood under which can be seen the Virgin Mary, Joseph, the Infant Jesus and the Shepherds. On January 6th three more people are added—the Magi. These cribs often have, besides their natural charm, a real artistic appeal, when each of the minute heroes of the nativity scene is what is called a "santon." These are simple peasant carvings made in Provence which portray with charming realism, and yet with poetry too, local types of people: the village drummer, the gamekeeper, the mayor with his tricolor belly-band, the local gossip, the Provençal bull-keeper on horseback, the postman, all coming to worship the Infant Jesus. These homely figures take us by the hand and lead us to Christmas in Provence: Christmas in the sunniest part of France. No fir trees here, but olive trees. In the vast fireplaces of the hall of the "mas" (the Provençal term for a farm) they burn the yule log and spend the night sitting round it. The yule log is a huge piece of olive tree thoroughly dried and carefully chosen because it is the most beautiful, the very finest. It will blaze up, bright and sweetly perfumed. The peasants, returning from Midnight Mass, cluster round the fire. And the grandfather tells old country legends while all drink great bowls of wine, warm and spiced. And everyone sings those Provençal Christmas songs which are among the loveliest in French folk music and in our regional poetry.

In the towns, Christmas Eve supper is a great tradition. First of all you go to Midnight Mass, the three low Masses, then parents and friends return home where Christmas Eve supper is waiting for them. The menu for this feast is pretty well the same each year.

It is generally oysters, black or mealy pudding, goose or turkey with chestnuts, *foie-gras* with salad, and rounded off with the so-called "yule log." This is an oblong cake covered with a thick layer of chocolate, marked to look like the bark of a tree.

At the party that follows the Christmas Eve supper, punch made of rum poured on sliced oranges and set alight used to make for shouts of delight.

★ ★ ★ ★ ★

In the Tropics—Nigeria (DENNIS OSADEBAY)

The rays of the tropical sun pierce through the misty clouds. The sky is not its usual cloudless blue: for it is December and the wind called Harmattan, blowing from the Sahara Desert, fills the air with fine dust. Flowers and trees are covered with dust, rivers parched, cattle drowsy. There are Africans dressed in flowing robes of silk or damask, or lightly clad in various designs of Manchester and Indian cotton. There is colour everywhere. This is the setting you have for Christmas in Nigeria.

The vast Nigerian territory—370,000 miles in area—covers mangrove swamps and sand beaches on the coast, followed by a belt of evergreen forest with its glorious palm trees and palm birds chirping merrily from leaf to leaf. Then it thins out into the savannah of the Northern Provinces beyond the hills, rivers and vast plateaux of rich farming lands and tin-fields. You find a people simple and generous, living close to nature and unspoilt by the evil side of modern industrialism. You will be greeted by people who always wear a smile.

The influence of Western civilization is making itself felt everywhere. When the British came they gradually instituted social services, schools, hospitals, law-courts, and they brought with them Christianity. Before that there were two kinds of religion practised. The Hausas of the North, one of the three major so-called tribes, drew their inspiration across the Sahara from the Orient and adopted the religion of Islam. This was embraced by some people in the Yoruba country in the West. But the Ibos and the "tribes" of the Eastern Provinces were untouched by the faith of the Mohammedans and worshipped the Great God (CHI-UKWU) through the ancestors. When Christianity came, it did not succeed in dislodging the Moslem religion but it found a ready response in the community of the non-Moslems, who found it comparatively easy to substitute for the worship of God through the ancestors the worship of God through the saints.

The Moslems still held their Ramadan, or the Feast of the New Year, and other festivals. But just as Christmas replaced the ancient pagan festival of Yuletide in Europe, so it replaced, or rather is replacing, the feast of the New Yam or harvest festival, and other ancient festivals of Africa.

In Nigeria, Christmas is not celebrated by Christians alone. It has become a national festival and embraces all people whatever their faith. People save all through the year, and the banks have Christmas savings schemes. Shopping is as exciting as anywhere else. Shops are decorated for the occasion, and from gramophone shops can be heard the familiar Christmas hymns and carols, known all over the world—"Adeste Fideles," "The First Noel," "Silent Night." And even "Good King Wenceslas" is hummed or whistled by shoppers or passers-by who had never seen, and, perhaps, will never see snow "deep and crisp and even." Fine clothes and jewellery are bought for the occasion, and so are food and drink.

The staple food is yam or farina (flour made from cassava), but during the Christmas season rice must be provided by rich and poor. There is poultry as in England. Those who cannot afford turkey provide chicken. But the well-to-do families consider turkey too humble for such an important occasion as Christmas, and so slaughter goats or sheep or cows, sending portions of the uncooked meat to relatives or friends all over the town or village. Christmas dinner consists mainly of meat and rice, fruits, sweets and biscuits, served to anyone who cares to call. The housewife is kept very busy, for she has to throw her doors open to all well-wishers and neighbours.

On Christmas Eve, when the golden rays of the tropical sun begin to disappear behind the hills and men and women have returned from their offices, workshops and farms, the fun begins. Nigerians know little about Guy Fawkes, so the children play all their pranks with fireworks on Christmas or New Year's Eve. Drummers and various groups parade the streets singing and dancing. The singing, the shouts of children, and barks and whistles of fireworks make one feel as if everybody was in the streets. The singers sing familiar carols and Nigerian folk songs, and call on important people in the community who give them presents of all kinds, usually money. Anyone not visited by these singing bands considers himself slighted.

The Roman Catholics hold their midnight mass on Christmas Eve whilst the Protestants hold their midnight service on New Year's Eve. Cribs may be found in Roman Catholic churches and homes. On Christmas morning, church bells peal, calling their members to Christmas service, or mass. Non-Christians, and Christians who do not go, continue the carnival, to be joined later by those returning from church.

Let us imagine ourselves standing in Tinubu Square, the Piccadilly Circus of Lagos, the capital of Nigeria. In front of us stands the huge building that houses the Law Courts: on the left stands the Tinubu Methodist Church, its red-roofed tower smiling to the morning sun. Behind it in Odunlami Street, not seen from where we stand, is the Anglican Cathedral where sits the British Bishop of Lagos. It is eleven o'clock in the morning. Buses, taxis, private cars, and hundreds of cyclists find their way slowly among pedestrians streaming out of church, all imbued with the Christmas spirit. There is brilliant colour everywhere—all the colours of the rainbow are there in the ladies' head-kerchiefs, frocks, jumpers and loincloths. The church bell is chiming. From Victoria Street, on the right, comes the sound of a brass band playing an exciting African rhythm. The band leader is dressed like the Pied Piper of Hamelin, on his lips a brass trumpet reflecting the light of the sun. Behind him dance masqueraders wearing masks and fancy costumes. Cars, buses, and cyclists have had to stop. Pedestrians crowd to watch the procession. Old mothers, girls and boys cannot resist the music. They join in the fun, with Bibles and prayer books in their hands. Everyone is dancing now. Some give money to the band leader. There is laughter everywhere. The helpless traffic police shake their heads and stand aside, and from the cars, taxis and buses, coloured handkerchiefs wave in the air as the occupants break forth into singing. And this happens to a greater or lesser degree in other parts of the town and in other towns and villages throughout the country.

In Nigeria, Christmas brings happiness to every heart. The children have their presents, but Santa Claus doesn't bring them. Instead they call on relatives and friends of their families, and return home in the evening their arms laden with parcels and their pockets jingling with coins. Other presents arrive by post. A visitor coming to England from Nigeria is surprised by the quietness of the streets on Christmas or Christmas Eve. He is surprised to find Christmas a family affair during which time families gather round their own home fires, for in Nigeria it is a communal affair when people go out into the streets, making merry, forgiving old grudges and making new friends. It is the season when township by-laws about drumming and processions are suspended to give the people freedom to give expression to their own ideas of peace and goodwill in the true African way, with pageantry, music and dancing.

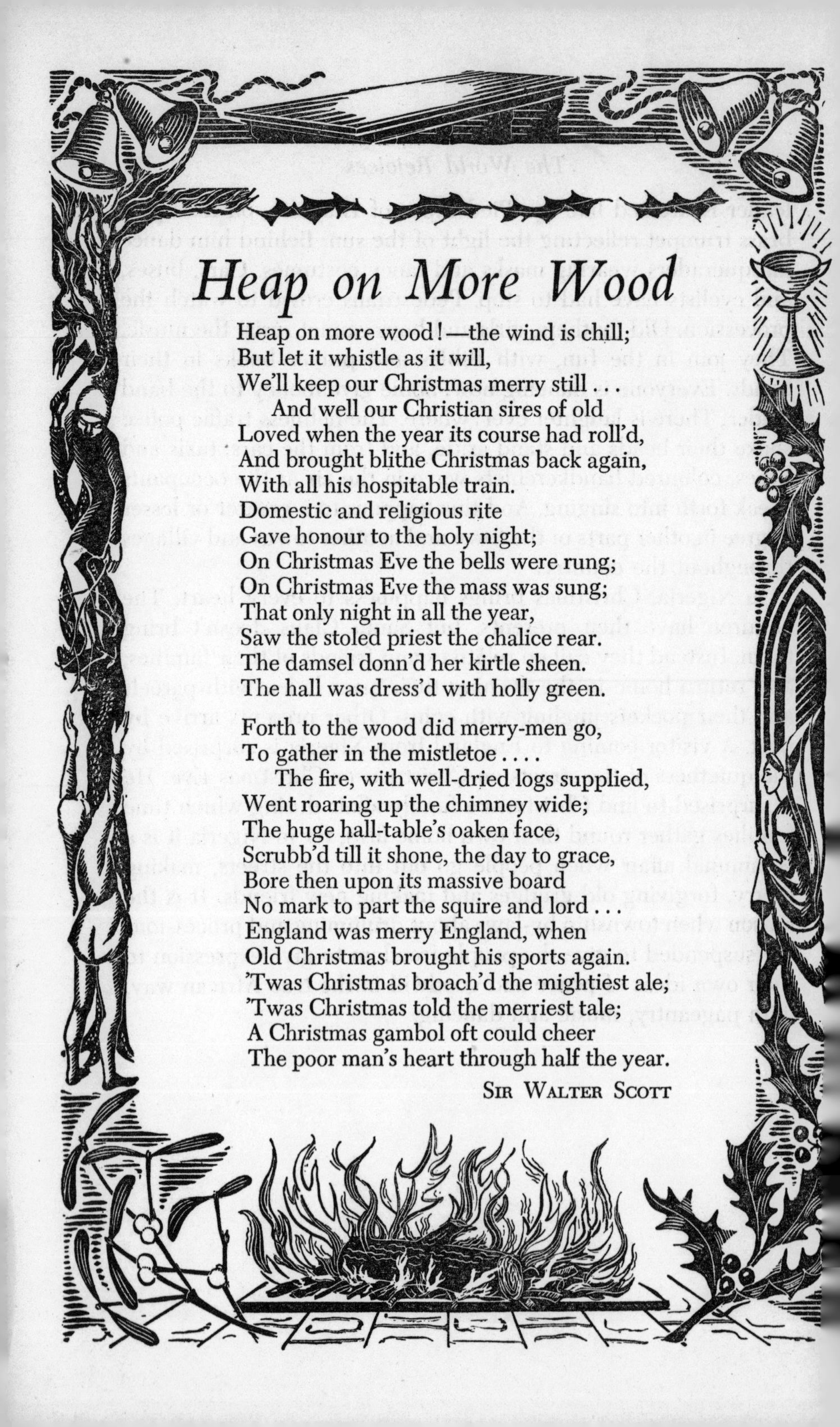

Heap on More Wood

Heap on more wood!—the wind is chill;
But let it whistle as it will,
We'll keep our Christmas merry still . . .
  And well our Christian sires of old
Loved when the year its course had roll'd,
And brought blithe Christmas back again,
With all his hospitable train.
Domestic and religious rite
Gave honour to the holy night;
On Christmas Eve the bells were rung;
On Christmas Eve the mass was sung;
That only night in all the year,
Saw the stoled priest the chalice rear.
The damsel donn'd her kirtle sheen.
The hall was dress'd with holly green.

Forth to the wood did merry-men go,
To gather in the mistletoe . . . .
  The fire, with well-dried logs supplied,
Went roaring up the chimney wide;
The huge hall-table's oaken face,
Scrubb'd till it shone, the day to grace,
Bore then upon its massive board
No mark to part the squire and lord . . .
England was merry England, when
Old Christmas brought his sports again.
'Twas Christmas broach'd the mightiest ale;
'Twas Christmas told the merriest tale;
A Christmas gambol oft could cheer
The poor man's heart through half the year.

SIR WALTER SCOTT